BIO-EN[...]
HEALING

Therapy of the Future

Katie Burns

Healing Touch Centre

4890033.

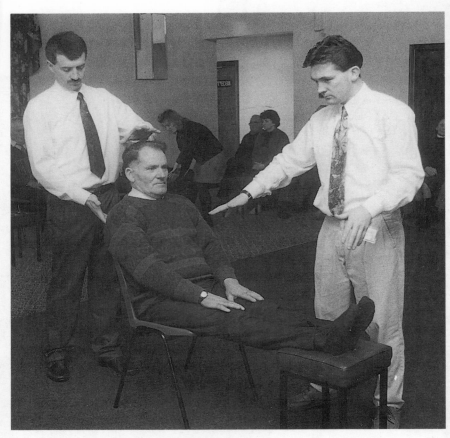

In a scene from a typical clinic, Michael O'Doherty and Tom Griffin channel
healing energy into the energy field of a patient, Michael Walshe. This position
is ideal for this 'energising' process, and this process will in turn restore
the body's natural ability to heal itself.

BIO-ENERGY HEALING

Therapy of the Future

MICHAEL O'DOHERTY
AND
TOM GRIFFIN

Edited by
DEREK DUNNE

THE O'BRIEN PRESS
DUBLIN

First published 1991 by The O'Brien Press Ltd.,
20 Victoria Road, Rathgar, Dublin 6, Ireland.

10 9 8 7 6 5 4 3 2 1

British Library Cataloguing in Publication Data
Griffin, Tom
Bio-energy healing.
1. Healing
I. Title II. O'Doherty, Michael
615.5
ISBN 0-86278-244-9

Cover design: Catherine Henderson
Drawings: Catherine Henderson
Typesetting: The O'Brien Press Ltd
Separations: The City Office, Dublin
Printing: Colour Books Ltd., Dublin

*Michael dedicates the book to
'my parents and family'.
Tom dedicates the book to
'my wife, parents and family'.*

Acknowledgements

We would like to extend a special word of thanks here to our staff. Without their dedication and support, it just would not be possible to bring the therapy to the number of people we are currently treating. So a special thanks to Tina, Anette, Colm, Bridie, Noreen, Michael, J J, Maureen, Pat, Stephen, Alan, Michael O'Doherty Snr, Helen Green in Birmingham, Joe Hurley and Michael Keane in Doonbeg, P J, Laurence, Kathy and Selena. And we would like to say thank you to our parents and families for their initial encouragement and continuing support for bio-energy therapy. Without that initial support it is doubtful that we would have been as successful in popularising the therapy. The O'Connor family in Banóg in Croom, Co Limerick, also deserve our thanks for their support and help down through the years.

We would also like to thank the O'Donovan family, in Grange Upper, Newcastlewest, Co Limerick. It was four years ago that they set up the first clinic for Michael O'Doherty. Martin Byrnes in the *Limerick Leader* also deserves a special word of thanks because it was he who first gave us very favourable media coverage at a time when we needed it most.

We would like to thank Gay Byrne and The Late Late Show for all the help they gave us, but especially Brigid Ruane, whose research and hard work helped us enormously. Thanks also to Roisin Harkin on the Show.

There are many others in the media who gave us encouragement and help when we needed it. Among those we would like to thank are Clare FM, Midwest Radio, Wexford Radio, Horizon Radio, Gerry Wilson on 2FM, Elvira Sterle of Radio Zadar in Yugoslavia and Sue Farrington of BBC Channel 5 Radio. Jim Fahy of RTE's Six One News also has our appreciation.

There is a very large number of people – too numerous to mention – who gave us help and facilities which enabled us to set up clinics. There is, for example, Pat Colgan of the Spa Hotel in Lucan, Co Dublin. His generosity and on-going support ensures that the people of Dublin have a chance to avail of bio-energy therapy. There are others we would like to thank here.

They include Tommy and Brigid Tubridy of Tubridy's Lounge of Doonbeg, Co Clare; the owners and staff of the Rosslevyn Arms, Ennis, Co Clare; The Belmont Hotel, Knock, Co Mayo; The Castlecourt Hotel, Co Wexford; Barney's of Castlebridge, Co Wexford; John McParland and The Carrickdale Hotel, Dundalk, Co Louth; The Ark Tavern, Limerick City; The Oranmore Lodge, Oranmore, Co Galway.

The Keenan family of Wexford also deserve our thanks for all the help they have given us. A very special mention must also go to the Walsh family of The Raftery Rooms, Kiltimagh, Co Mayo. Throughout, they have been a source of unflagging support, and continue to encourage us in all our endeavours.

Dusam Ostojic in Yugoslavia has also helped us. We would also like to thank Professor Drago Culina, Yugoslav radio and television presenter and director.

Michael Commins and Dave Mullins also helped when we needed it. Jim Higgins TD was also a source of encouragement.

Michael Costigan and his family were a great help to us. And a special mention and thanks to our friend P J McEvoy, who proved supportive and loyal. The Green family in Birmingham made it possible to set up the first bio-energy clinic outside Ireland and we want to thank them for their generosity and support. The staff of Saint Anne's Centre in Birmingham also made our stay a welcome one. There are many, many people who helped us along the way and in a sense, this book is dedicated to all of them. No matter where we went, we found nothing but encouragement and support for what we were doing. It is with their help that we will popularise this therapy further. With the publication of this book, we are not at the end of the journey. This book has really only set the foundation for the development of the therapy in the future.

To all those who helped in any way, no matter how small, thanks. But thanks most of all to the patients who had enough faith in the treatment to attend our clinics. They have made bio-energy the therapy of the future.

Contents

Tom Griffin treating Kathleen McCoy. In this standing position, Tom uses his hands to balance the energy field from front to back. This is necessary if the health of the patient is to be restored. Sometimes a patient may feel a pull either to the front or back.

INTRODUCTION

The aim of this book is to explain to as wide an audience as possible what bio-energy therapy is all about and how it works. We hope that it will dispel some of the myths surrounding the therapy and go some way towards explaining a phenomenon which is uniquely placed to assist a great number of people in regaining their health and happiness. We believe that this form of therapy is vitally important, may even be the therapy of the future, and that within a short space of time it will come to play an integral part in the treatment of many diseases and conditions. Scores of patients, referred to us by general practitioners, have already been treated successfully and it is only a matter of time before even greater numbers of the medical profession come to accept this form of therapy as valid.

Bio-energy therapy is unique among 'alternative', or complementary, methods of treatment. One of the main differences between it and other therapies (such as faith healing) is that anybody can be taught how to administer it successfully. This is not the case with other therapies, many of which are dependent on abilities vested in individuals which are impossible to teach or pass on. Basically, any person who is healthy, both physically and mentally, should be able to administer bio-energy therapy and therefore help those whom they care for.

In order to understand what bio-energy is and how it works, the single most important attribute is an open mind on the part of those who would understand it. This is not to say that what is needed is a blind faith; on the contrary, there is ample scientific evidence concerning the existence of an energy field contained within the human body and around it – the natural energy of the universe. This is what we mean by bio-energy or the life energy. There is also scientific evidence and many documented cases to show that this human energy field can be manipulated and changed in such a way as to affect the health of an individual. A condition that manifests itself at the physical level will also disturb the energy levels of the body and it is possible to measure this. Electronic equipment, capable of measuring minute amounts of electricity and electromagnetic current, can pick up these energy exchanges using biosensors. This does not mean that bio-energy is an objective treatment and that everything that takes place can be quantified, but it does show that science can at least measure some part of what is happening.

What we mean here by an open mind is one which accepts that phenomena exist which science cannot quantify or measure at this time. In the future, science may well be able to explain bio-energy, using strict scientific criteria, but at present this type of research is in its infancy. For now, we must simply accept that there is more in the universe than we can see. While few people are actually privileged enough to be able to see the human energy field, many are able to feel it while the therapy is being performed on them. But even if people are unable to either see or feel it, this does not stop us utilising this life energy in ways which help people to recover from their illness.

CHAPTER 1

Origins

❋

B IO-ENERGY IS NOT a new phenomenon. It has been the
subject of serious study in China and other Eastern countries for thousands of years. The Chinese refer to this energy
as 'Ch'i' and they have formulated theories as to how exactly
it circulates in the body. This circulation system is quite
complicated, but the main energy flow is from the base of
the spine to the top of the head, and vice versa. Contained
in this two-way energy channel are seven major energy
centres, which are, in turn, linked to fourteen energy-gather-
ing centres. Bio-energy therapy acts on all of these energy
centres.

The first reference to the life energy is in the *I Ching* ('The
Book of Changes'), introduced into China some time before
1122 BC. The *I Ching* discussed three types of energy in broad
terms: cosmic energy, earth energy and human energy. The
discovery that human energy was a mixture of both earth
and cosmic energy led to the further discovery that there was
a measurable relationship between the three types of energy
and that it was possible for people to manipulate them.

Around 300 BC, it was known that people in China were
using certain breathing techniques to control and manipulate these energies. Such exercises were used at first to
maintain health in the individual concerned, but a secondary benefit was found to be that illness could be cured in
others. Both were done by changing the quantity and quality
of the energy levels within the human system. (It is interesting to note that the study of the energies had no religious
overtones at this time.) The training people underwent to
become proficient in this therapy was a natural training and

their way of improving health was strictly nature-based; there was no recourse to chemicals or anything alien to the body. Regrettably, there are few documents available from this period to detail either the training techniques or the developments.

Around AD 58, Buddhism was introduced into China and was quickly integrated into the people's culture. The meditation techniques of Buddhism were married to the study of the life energy, leading to much new knowledge. Unlike previously, these new developments were kept from the general public by the Buddhist monks, who locked away their secrets behind monastery walls. One of the main reasons for this seems to have been that the monks' training, being strictly religious, enabled them to use the life energy to attain a higher state of consciousness. They did not appear to be overly concerned about the health of the masses or in trying to help them reach a better understanding of the energies around them. Instead, the monks concentrated their efforts on trying to escape from the endless cycle of reincarnation to which they believed all human beings were subjected. They worked with the life energy at a very deep level and tried to control the various functions of the body (including the internal organs and the ageing process) by manipulating this energy. It is not known how successful they were at slowing down the ageing process, but there are certainly numerous reports of monks living well past the age of 100. Thus the theory concerning the circulation of energy, both inside and outside the body – crucial to the healing process – as well understood by this time, but only by a select few who had erected a wall of silence between themselves and the vast majority of the populace.

The next phase in the study and use of the life energy was its integration with training in the martial arts. Study and understanding of this energy force was found to enhance fighting technique and many different styles of martial arts developed at this time. Theories surrounding the circulation of the life energy abounded and many documents were published relating to the medical uses to which the energy might be put. But the deeper knowledge which the monks had gathered was still hidden from the public: the uses to which the life energy was put in religious circles remained totally secret and the training undergone by the monks was generally much harsher than most other occupations. By now, however, the basic exercises had become popular within Chinese society and remained so right up until 1911.

At this time, China began to make serious efforts to embrace the outside world. The Ching dynasty was overthrown in 1911 and certain documents that had remained secret for hundreds of years began to circulate outside China. These documents became widely available during the following decades, but it is only in the last ten to twenty years that the significance of what the Chinese had learned over the past 4000 years began to be appreciated in the West. Incidentally, China was not the only country to develop theories about the existence and use of the life energy. Chinese methods of energy control are today being compared with similar methods developed in India, Korea, Japan and the Middle East.

The knowledge that the Chinese possessed was put to various uses at different times. But the single most important point was that they could manipulate the life energy through the use of concentration and will. This gave them a degree of control over their physical, mental, emotional and spiritual well-being. In addition, it allowed those who had the knowledge to help others who suffered various diseases and conditions. The life energy, or bio-energy, became the bedrock on which Chinese medicine was built.

EASTERN APPROACHES VERSUS WESTERN

The fact that bio-energy has only been discovered relatively recently in the West has meant that Western science has not had the opportunity to study the phenomenon in detail. What scientists have tried to do is to measure the energy when it is being used successfully to cure diseases which conventional medicine is unable to treat. Despite the fact that the study of the life energy is so ancient, there are still many questions that remain unanswered as to how and why bio-energy therapy works, even among its most experienced practitioners. The basic movements and techniques employed by therapists cannot be explained using conventional terminology. It is only possible to say that an 'exchange of energy' takes place. Although science is only now beginning to develop the technology that will eventually add to the knowledge already available, there are a number of points worth making at the outset in relation to current and future developments.

Our lack of knowledge about bio-energy is not so surprising when you consider the fact that Chinese culture and medicine only became common knowledge in the West in the early 1970s. There followed a massive interest in all Oriental forms of medicine and healing. Dramatic scenes were shown on television of patients undergoing major surgery in China with their only anaesthetic consisting of some needles inserted here and there in the body. The nature of these pictures tended to shift the focus away from the underlying principles involved in the art of acupuncture, various forms of massage and the notion of life energy. The fact that a patient was able to sit up and chat with the surgeon during the operation looked, to the Western eye at least, more like some form of magician's trick than any sort of serious medicine.

The extraordinary nature of Chinese medicine may baffle the Western mind, but to the Chinese it is perfectly normal. Their system of health care has developed in quite a different way to that of the West. They have always understood and accepted the concept that the mind has an effect on the body and that therefore an untreated mental problem could eventually manifest itself in a physical disorder. (In contrast, mental ill heath is a relatively recent notion in Western medicine, popularised by psychologists such as Jung and Freud; up to then, those that complained of a disease that did not manifest itself somehow in the physical body were thought to be either malingerers or mad.) What the Chinese believe, in relation to the mind having an effect on the body, should not be confused with psychosomatic illnesses, where physical disorders are believed by the patient to be present but for which there is no corresponding independent medical verification.

The Chinese belief centres around the theory that a mental problem causes an imbalance of energy in the body and that unless this imbalance is corrected, then the physical body will eventually succumb to a disorder indirectly related to this imbalance. The initial energy imbalance can come about in any number of ways, but it is accepted that in order to be healthy again the imbalance has to be corrected. Thus, crucial to understanding the life energy is the belief that the energy imbalance *causes* the illness and not the other way around.

Nowadays, Western medicine accepts that the mind does have an effect on the body, apart altogether from the psychosomatic area. This is particularly apparent in the area of heart complaints. Conventional medical practitioners agree that a sense of calm in the patient may go some way towards stabilising certain heart conditions; the calm necessary to reduce the risk of an attack is brought about by a mental attitude and this takes some time to achieve. The West has much to learn from the East in this area; after all, the East has had a 4000-year start.

One of the problems in this learning process is the different terms used to describe various conditions in the two different cultures. For example, when a patient has a 'heart condition' in the West, it is usually only that organ which is treated. In China, on the other hand, the treatment of such a patient would also involved his emotional, mental and spiritual well-being. The only common factor in the two very different approaches is the word 'heart'. While it is true to say that the real difficulty is in the interpretation of the terms, the terms themselves have also caused problems in the past and will continue to do so for as long as our understanding is as limited as it is.

For many centuries, the Chinese were an inward-looking people. Their spiritual yearning led them to study the energy that was contained in the human body and they came to the view that there was a link between that energy and the energy of nature, which could help to cure illness in the body. Mental, emotional and spiritual well-being were considered part and parcel of a physically healthy person; no one aspect could be treated in isolation from the other aspects. Their beliefs were heavily influenced by Buddhism and the overall thrust of their society was towards the spiritual rather than the materialistic. Eastern medicine has therefore always been concerned with this total balance and it views physical diseases and conditions as resulting potentially from a lack of energy balance at one or several levels.

Exactly the opposite view developed in the West. Here, the physical body and its various parts were treated in isolation by medical practitioners, while religion was left to cater for the mental, emotional and spiritual well-being of the individual. What evolved was a system whereby the different aspects of the human being were dealt with separately by secular and clerical institutions. The symptoms of physical disorders were treated, with few attempts to examine the causes and link all the various aspects together as a whole.

A simple example will serve to illustrate. The Chinese have known for thousands of years that worry and nervousness can cause problems in the stomach area. Again we have the difficulty of terminology, since the Chinese are not talking strictly about the stomach itself but about the whole system of functions that relate to and affect the digestive system.

Western medicine has now come to accept that stress can cause ulcers and other disorders.

Good health in the East has always been linked to a healthy mind and a healthy body. A person's total needs are examined, not just the immediate symptoms. On the basis that emotions can affect the physical body, or mental attitudes affect the emotions, these elements are not possible to separate and treat individually. In order to achieve the required balance for health, concentration and will are used to balance a person's energy and to manipulate that energy to bolster internal strength, whether for spiritual purposes or to repair internal organs and speed up the healing process in others.

WHAT IS BIO-ENERGY?

Bio-energy has been defined throughout the ages in various different ways. The definitions often depend on the person's background and the area of research in which they are engaged. For example, some describe it as an electromagnetic energy, others as an electric energy, while still others say that it is a form of heat or light. Put as simply as possible, we say it is the natural life energy that fills the universe. It is made up of cosmic energy, such as sunshine and moonlight, and earth energy, which is made up of the energy that comes from within the earth itself and that surrounds the planet. Earth energy is influenced, and to some extent controlled, by cosmic energy. This is easier to accept when one considers, for example, the effect the moon has on the tides or indeed on human behaviour.

The definition of bio-energy is not, however, a crucial factor. We appreciate that the study of the life energy takes a long time and that the most important application to date – in the area of human health – is only one of the many possible applications that the manipulation of the energy can have. But this life energy is the source of all life and once a person has learned how it works and how to manipulate it, they may lead long and healthy lives.

The Chinese study of geomancy holds that the earth energy, in addition to comprising the earth's magnetic field, is also composed of lines and patterns of energy and heat concealed underground. It is believed that in those places where the earth's own energy is balanced, plants and animals, including human beings, thrive. Conversely, where the earth's energies are out of balance living things do not thrive. Specialists have been employed in this area of study for centuries in choosing, for example, the best possible sites for shrines or houses or whatever human endeavour is being undertaken.

Going on from those two energies, every single living thing has its own energy field or 'aura' which exists within the earth's energy field. The energy field of living things also goes to make up part of the entire energy field on the earth. The most important point to be made here about the human energy field is that it always seeks to be balanced, to be healthy. This is the central underlying concept behind bio-energy therapy. When an individual loses that balance, he or she will get sick and may die unless the energy is balanced again, either through their own efforts or somebody else's. When people's energies are in balance, they will be at one with nature. This awareness may not be an entirely conscious thing, but people who are in balance and harmony with themselves and their surroundings will have a knowledge and a respect for their planet.

The energy contained inside and outside the human body is different to the earth and cosmic energies in so far as it is made up of a fusion of the last two energies and has been refined to a state where it can be utilised by the body. (Naturally enough, people have been more preoccupied through the ages with their own energy fields than with the energy fields of the earth or other energies around them.) The basic theory is that the two types of energy, cosmic and earth, flow through the body in a predetermined way; when there is a blockage in the major energy centres, the energy cannot continue to flow freely and ill health will result.

In general, all energy comes from matter as a result of some kind of chemical reaction. It is the unlocked potential of matter and manifests itself as either heat, light or electro-magnetic force. Those who have learned to control and manipulate the energy inside and outside the human body describe its behaviour as being similar to water. Like a river running its course, energy flows freely in the healthy body from the areas of highest potential to the areas of lowest potential. What this means in practical terms is that the energy will first enter the most important areas of the body, those most necessary for survival, and then pass on to those parts of secondary importance. This means that a natural balancing process is going on all the time.

HOW ENERGY AFFECTS HEALTH

In order to explain how the mind has an effect on the body, we can use the analogy of water again. If water is left undisturbed, any sediment will settle to the bottom, leaving the water clear. If the water is stirred up, however, it becomes murky. This is similar to what happens when the mind is disturbed – the body's energy will be distorted and uneven. When the mind is calm and clear, the body's energies are undisturbed and free-flowing. The energy channels which supply energy to the body are often compared to rivers and the centres which store the energy to reservoirs. The energy flow within the human body should be continuous and smooth; when a channel is obstructed, the flow of energy is agitated and uneven, often leading to a blockage.

Energy contained in the human body can become too strong or too weak. When there is a weakness, this indicates a depletion of energy which can be rectified by putting more in. When the energy is too strong, it can be balanced by taking some out. This will be explained in greater detail later on. In general, different organs of the body require different levels of energy. The heart, lungs, kidneys, liver, spleen and pericardium, for example, require a lower level of energy than the large and small intestines, stomach, gall bladder and urinary bladder.

WHAT AFFECTS ENERGY LEVELS

The energy level within the body can be affected by many different factors, including the weather, climate and seasonal changes. Other cycles that affect the human energy field are the cycles of night and day, the rotation of the earth, the monthly lunar cycles and the yearly cycle. Every twelve and sixty years, such cycles as the rotation of the stars also influence us, but they are more difficult to relate to our energy fields because of the lengths of time involved.

Because we live within the earth's magnetic field, and since our bodies also have a magnetic field, our energy field is affected by that of the earth. This can be proved by scientific experiment. Science has already shown that electrical and magnetic fields cannot be separated and are really aspects of the same force – where one is present, so is the other. This type of field is called an electromagnetic field. A simple scientific experiment shows that when a piece of steel or any good conductor of electricity is placed inside a magnetic field, it becomes a magnet. And since we are in the magnetic field of the earth, our bodies also act like magnets. The centre line of any magnet has two opposing poles. Similarly, the human body has two magnetic poles – one on the top of the head and the other at the base of the spine, corresponding to two of the major energy centre or 'chakras'.

It is important to stress that while there is ample scientific proof for the existence of this human energy field, both inside and outside the body, science is still a long way from being able to quantify what happens during bio-energy therapy. But yesterday's unexplained phenomenon can be today's familiar fact. So too with bio-energy: there are explanations about the life energy that may not coincide with any currently known scientific fact, but this does not mean that they should be rejected as being untrue. Our view of the world has a way of changing as more information comes to light.

CHAPTER 2

Harnessing the Life Energy

❁

Bio-energy therapy in the West was developed by Zdenko Domancic, a Yugoslavian who became interested in this form of healing through his involvement with the martial arts. The study of the life energy was part of his training and he continued to study the energy as developed by other civilisations and cultures. When he had rediscovered the art of self-healing, he brought it back to his native country and began to run clinics. In one eight-month period, some 50,000 people were treated. Because of the results achieved there, an upsurge of public interest led Domancic to give many open lectures and interviews to the press, radio and television so that bio-energy as a therapy could be fully appreciated. Initially, the response to his clinics had been one of scepticism, suspicion and doubt, but after the success of his treatments and his willingness for public discussion, attitudes changed to the extent that bio-energy therapy now enjoys the active support of doctors, scientists, lawyers and artists.

Domancic's holistic approach to health has been one in which people are treated with bio-energy therapy to the point where they can be helped by conventional medicine again or other complementary methods. This approach inspired the Centre for the Prevention and Treatment of Drug Addiction at the Clinic for Psychiatry, Neurology and Addiction in Belgrade to invite Domancic to visit the hospital and discuss the possibilities of using bio-energy therapy there. Domancic started to treat a number of patients at the Clinic and the doctor responsible for monitoring the experiment noted that the condition of all 38 patients had 'improved'; he recommended that Domancic should be allowed to continue the therapy with other patients.

This situation, where several varied disciplines had come together with the common aim of helping sick people get better, did not develop overnight. In December 1985, Domancic had convened the first public meeting in Yugoslavia which attempted to bring together representatives from all the 'border areas of science'. Interest in the meeting was overwhelming, with 6000 people turning up to fill a hall that seated only 200. There was also considerable interest from the established medical profession.

Immediately following this meeting, problems developed that would have been difficult to foresee. Many people claimed that they had an excess of energy – that they could feel it in their hands and that they had an urge to transfer it to people who had a deficiency of energy. This reawakening of people's inherent abilities was encouraging, but the idea they had of 'excess' energy was incorrect. No one has 'excess' energy in that sense of the word; people may have a blockage of energy at one or several centres, but this does not amount to excess energy. The energy that is used to help people comes from outside the person, from the earth and the atmosphere; the person carrying out the therapy is merely a conduit for that energy, not the originator of it. It was therefore a source of regret for Domancic that some people believed they could effectively monopolise a therapy that could be used to help others. Thus, the underlying basis for the therapy was being ignored in much the same way as the dramatic pictures of surgery being performed using acupuncture had obscured the real significance of the use of the life energy.

Two years later, in May 1987, Domancic founded the Society for the Investigation of Borderline Regions of Science and Mental Hygiene. The Society consists of medical doctors, physiotherapists and therapists, and investigates what is considered to be on the fringes of science. Its aim is to help heal people using bio-energy and other therapies in conjunction with the established sciences.

In that same year we travelled to Yugoslavia to meet Domancic, having discovered bio-energy therapy through our own involvement with the martial arts. We trained extensively with him and then returned to Ireland to set up bio-energy clinics, with the aim of giving people back responsibility for their own health.

THE PHILOSOPHY BEHIND BIO-ENERGY AND HOLISTICS

To understand bio-energy therapy, it is also necessary to appreciate the philosophy that has evolved in both the East and the West. Bio-energy therapy is non-denominational and thus its success or otherwise has nothing to do with a person's religious beliefs or lack of them.

The unique and basic aim of the therapy is to realise the potential of the individual to the full, so as to ensure that he or she enjoys good health and lives life in dignity. Bio-energy works by activating the person's own inherent ability to heal themselves. Everyone possesses this ability, but in most it lies dormant for a variety of reasons.

Generally, it is this ability to heal oneself that is ignored by conventional medical treatment, which often still regards the human being as being made up of a series of parts, one or more of which has broken down and needs fixing with drugs. Thus individuals are separated from their background and other influences (such as severe emotional trauma, instability at home, insecurity in a job) that may have been a cause of their ill health. In our experience, such influences are rarely taken into account by conventional medicine.

This brings us to another important point in relation to bio-energy therapy. We do not believe that bio-energy, or any other single discipline, has a monopoly on the way people should be treated. The bio-energy approach to health care is one which envelops the total human being – mental, spiritual, emotional and physical. The primary consideration is an holistic approach to the health of the individual which involves various disciplines coming together to realise that aim. This means that medical science, reflexologists, herbalists, bio-energy therapists and so on all cooperate in attempting to help people regain their health.

Implicit in this holistic approach is that all forms of health care should welcome constructive criticism and well-meaning advice. In this way, the holistic approach can develop and thrive, with no single discipline feeling that they have a monopoly on health care. Unfortunately, this is not the position at present. One of the main reasons for this, at least in the West, is the massive reliance by today's society on drugs, with the drug companies maximising their profits. Putting a price on people's health has led people to believe that health has a price, that it can be bought, and that they no longer have a responsibility for their own health. The truth of the matter is that, ultimately, the answer lies within people themselves.

The fact that we all have an inherent ability to heal ourselves is a knowledge that must be rekindled in people. Following bio-energy therapy, a person's energies should be in balance and harmony. It is at this point that the person can assume responsibility for their future health. This is the case no matter what the condition or disease. This may sound idealistic or simplistic to some, but it is nothing more than the truth and must be accepted if you are to take responsibility for your own life. The importance of this idea, of being inherently able to heal yourself, cannot be overemphasized. The spread of this notion is something that will give hope to people and thereby engender an holistic approach to health.

SUCCESS WITH BIO-ENERGY

Those who have learned the techniques and practice of bio-energy therapy have come to regard each person as special. The therapy involves a particular approach to the patient's health; the nature of the illness itself does not matter. The therapy is an open-hearted approach and the really successful results have been achieved when our patients have the same attitude. This is not to suggest that people have to suspend all their scepticism, only that they are prepared to give themselves and the treatment a chance. Successful therapy nearly always results in a deep psychological change in a person, which can manifest itself in the way they look at life. This has been confirmed by many of our patients and we are able to go some way towards an explanation.

If a person has little regard for themselves, their family or friends or environment, their energies will be out of balance. Whatever the reason for this state of affairs, we have found that unless a change is brought about, matters usually remain as they are. This is because such a lack of harmony and imbalance of energy is largely dependent on the individual's psychological well-being. The aim of bio-energy therapy, apart altogether from balancing the energy field within the person so that they can heal themselves and thereby eliminate the immediate problem, is to develop the total person so that the original complaint will not recur. This is not to suggest that all illness is psychological, but it does emphasize the psychological aspect that comes into play once the illness has set in. This aspect can become as important as the original reason for the illness once it has imprinted itself on the mind of the person involved.

It is important to remind people of their own healing ability. This can be reawakened through the therapy, putting the patient in a position to refine their feelings and thus balance their life. The part bio-energy therapy plays in this healing process is simple: by balancing the person's energy field and thus restoring the body's natural ability to heal itself, the person regains the dignity and ability to be well again. This has a knock-on effect.

When people have gained this new insight into their own lives, they will be in a better position to appreciate the plight of others who are unwell. This happens when people come to understand the source of their illness and have felt the effects of the therapy in their lives. This has been proven to us time and again in our clinics.

Bio-energy therapy also fits neatly into the established and alternative medical therapies. If a person has just undergone surgery, a session of bio-energy therapy will help speed up the recovery and healing process. With people who are on medication, the therapy can obviate the necessity of drugs in some cases or at least cause a review of the dosage.

THE LIFE FORCE

There are several important points to be made about bio-energy. Firstly, every human being has a life force or energy which circulates both inside and outside the body. It supports us in everything we do – our thinking, movements and feelings. Without this force, we could not survive. Nobody has an excess of this energy.

In the West, we are not used to thinking about ourselves in terms of energy. Granted, we may say that we are 'full of energy' or we 'lack energy', but we are only referring to our physical bodies. Most of us are blissfully unaware of our energy centres and how they can affect our lives and well-being. The fact that we cannot see this energy and are unaware of its existence does not, of course, mean that it is not there and that it is not having a profound and lasting effect on every aspect of our lives.

When we become aware of this life energy and its effects, things are viewed in a totally different light. The amount of energy a person has is generally reflected in their personality. People who are depressed are said to have 'little energy for life' (not to be confused with someone who is tired after a hard day's work). The opposite is also apparent in some people who seem to have 'limitless energy'. In these two instances, we are talking about a possible imbalance in the depressed person's energy field and an energy system that is in harmony in the case of the 'full of life' person. Temperamental people who frequently 'let off steam' are, in a manner of speaking, releasing energy before it gets a chance to build up. If they kept their feelings pent in, this would eventually lead to imbalance and sickness. This is one way of keeping their energy field in balance.

To sum up, the most important point to grasp is that the way in which people utilise their energies is crucial to their health. A blockage of energy along the energy centres, or a depletion, will result in an energy disharmony within the body, which can leave the person open to disorder and disease.

BIO-ENERGY – WHO BENEFITS?

Most people who attend a bio-energy clinic have no idea what the treatment entails or how it works. In most instances, people have attended doctors and specialists, yet found no relief for their condition. They have lost faith in conventional medicine. They come to our clinic and do not know what to expect. In addition, they are not really aware that there are certain techniques and stipulations that govern the treatment, just as there are disciplines that govern conventional medicine.

An example of this would be where a person feels much better following a session of bio-energy therapy and on this basis decides to stop seeing his doctor. He does this of his own accord and it is something that worries us from time to time. We understand his reluctance to go back to his doctor and explain his improved condition using an alternative approach. But patients must realise that all genuinely caring doctors have an open mind about such therapies. This can be especially true in cases where a doctor can do little more for the patient and thus the patient has basically nothing to lose. The truth of the matter is that when a patient benefits from bio-energy therapy, this also helps the doctor.

Another important point is that patients who are on medication must return to their doctor so that the medication can be reviewed in the light of their changed condition. There are obvious dangers involved in not doing this: ceasing to take the medication or continuing to take the same dosage both have their risks.

Another good reason for people who have benefitted from bio-energy therapy to return to their doctor is for validation of the results. After all, it was the doctor who made the original diagnosis. In certain diseases and conditions, further medical treatment or rehabilitation is necessary; for example, in the case of a car accident, bio-energy therapy may have speeded up the healing process, but the patient may also need more physiotherapy to bring them a stage further. Again, in the case of people who have gained or regained their hearing, speech therapy will be necessary before they can be fully rehabilitated.

HARNESSING THE LIFE ENERGY

The best proof of the positive effects of bio-energy therapy are the testimonies of people who have benefitted from the treatment and we have many of these (see Chapter 7). But as important as the results is the theory behind the therapy, of how and why the life energy is harnessed to help people regain their health and retain it. The road to becoming and remaining healthy is a long and complex one, and bio-energy therapy can have different results with different people. Our experience has shown that no two people respond to the therapy in the same way.

The concept of energy-based therapy has only been recognised in the West since 1979, when the World Health Organization finally gave official recognition to acupuncture as a valid and acceptable method of treating people – a method that has been used in China for thousands of years. In recognising acupuncture, Western science has now implicitly accepted that meridians of energy flow exist within the body and that it is possible to harness that energy in the treatment of illness.

Although the methods of acupuncture are different to those of bio-energy, the theories behind both treatments are based on the same energy flows within the body and the manipulation of that energy. Bio-energy therapy is concerned with those areas that are left untouched by conventional medicine and other therapies. It is concerned with the underlying cause of an illness, not just the physical symptoms. In cases where the physical injury has an obvious physical cause, as in the case of a car-accident victim, the therapy can reduce the level of permanent damage to a person or even eliminate the damage altogether. This means that a vast range of diseases and disorders can be successfully treated with the therapy utilising the life energy present all around us.

Bio-energy therapy is not unique in using this life force. There are numerous examples in the Western world of people with extraordinary powers, from faith healers to religious figures, curing people by using this life force. The results of their work can be seen after the laying-on of hands on a sick person or even when a sick person comes into their presence. These healers may not even be conscious that what they are using is the life energy. Many people view this as a religious phenomenon, while others have sought a scientific explanation.

Psychoanalyst Wilhelm Reich spent years studying the life energy. He called it 'orgon' energy and believed that there was a unity between human beings and nature which was impossible to split without serious repercussions. He also believed that the life energy was all-present and that its flow changed only in density and concentration. He felt that by changing the concentration of energy or regulating it within the body, it was possible to use and control it to help those suffering from various diseases. Today, Reich's research into 'orgon' energy is being reinvestigated by scientists in, for example, the American Orgonomy College in the USA.

There are hundreds of institutes across the world which specialise in carrying out experiments in the areas that have been little explored in the West to date. Apart from bio-energy, other subjects, including psychokinesis, telepathy, psychometry and precognition, are under investigation. In the Soviet Union alone, there are more than 20 of these research institutes and it is to the credit of the Eastern Bloc countries that they have been studying this area for at least forty years. Similarly, the United States have been doing a considerable amount of research in this area. The common aim of all this work is to try and understand phenomena that are beyond the laws of science as those laws are currently laid down.

Up until 1968, the term 'parapsychology' was applied to this area of endeavour. Then a new term was coined – psychotronics. This is defined as a science which concerns itself with the interaction of living organisms (including human beings) and their external and internal environments. The human power to heal using bio-energy is one area under investigation and gradually the statistical proof is being assembled which will allow scientists to state that the unusual way of diagnosing and treating people using bio-energy exists and works.

HOW ENERGY FLOWS

The energy referred to by Reich and many others is a mixture of both earth energy and cosmic energy. Where the earth and cosmic energies meet and flux, a new and more powerful energy is created within the human being. This energy is utilised throughout the body, through the seven major and 21 minor energy centres. Lying slightly in front of the spine, the main energy centres take in energy in a spiralling motion and the unrestricted movement of that energy is the factor that determines health.

Everybody, whether they realise it or not, is sensitive and susceptible to these energies. The physical body is constantly surrounded by and feeding off such energy and without it we would not survive. The balance and unimpeded flow of energies runs from the top of the head to the base of the spine in the case of cosmic energy, and from the base of the spine to the top of the head in the case of earth energy. When people are standing up, they are in the best position to avail of both types of energy. While people are lying down, the energy flow into these areas is weaker and all the various functions of the body tend to slow down.

The pathways along which these energies travel are known as meridians. They are close to the nerves in the body and relate to the nerves in much the same way as a high-frequency current relates to the conductor. This needs to be explained: a current has a tendency to run along the surface of a conductor, such as a wire, and not through the centre, as many people think.

The earth and cosmic energies interact with each other and fuse to form a new type of energy, which is within and outside the body. This vital life energy enters the body in a spiralling motion and looks much a whirlpool or vortex. It takes on the characteristics of the living organism and is strongest in the areas of the brain, throat, heart, stomach and intestines. It is distributed through the meridians and from there to the organs and other parts of the body which need it. At the time of writing, there exist as many theories as theorists as to how the energy flows through the physical body. What we have outlined above is just one theory which we believe to be closest to the truth.

The energy in a healthy person is continually flowing and being transformed as a result of breathing, the circulation of blood and the actions of the central nervous system. But apart from these normal physical ways of circulating energy in the body, it is possible for the individual to direct and manipulate the life energy in either themselves or in somebody else by using their will. This is the key to bio-energy therapy and we will return to it at a later stage.

For the moment, we would like to deal more fully with the normal circulation of energy and some of the theories surrounding it. Blood circulation is crucial to the transformation of the energy from its raw state into a state in which the body can utilise it. This is perhaps one of the reasons why every civilisation has placed great emphasis on blood as the carrier of the life force. Traditional Chinese belief holds that the human being is composed of energy and matter, and that between the two lies blood, being considered energy and matter at one and the same time. Blood is responsible for cleansing and feeding the physical body; it flows into every part and takes away the waste and the poisons, presenting it with life. An important point here is that blood containing oxygen has paramagnetic features, which means that it takes on magnetic qualities but does not retain them. This helps us somewhat in our attempts to understand how the energy works. Oxygen is an active ingredient in the transformation of energy, but the activities of breathing, blood circulation and the central nervous system could not be carried out without the life energy which sustains them.

THE ENERGY CENTRES

The human being is a complex organism composed of various energies which are interrelated and mutually dependent. The energies are contained in, or come from, different processes. There are the energies contained in the physical body. Then there are the energies generated by our thought processes, which we generally recognise as our personality. Finally, there is the potential consciousness which is realised when we are in a state of deep contemplation and contentment. When we look at ourselves in this light, it is easy to see that there exists a huge potential within each of us and that by changing the way we think and project ourselves, we can affect our entire existence, including our health.

There are seven major energy centres in the human body, called 'chakras' in Eastern traditions. These centres are constantly taking in raw energy, refining it from a coarse to a more subtle state in which it can be carried by the blood and oxygen, and then distributing it to those parts of the body that need it. It is at the energy centres themselves that our physical and energy bodies merge and mix.

When a person has a session of bio-energy therapy, the healing process is activated at these centres through the will of the person administering the therapy. By balancing the energy in these centres, the entire energy field of the body is affected and put in balance. It is at this point that the energy is transformed into something which will allow people to heal themselves.

The locations of the seven major energy centres correspond to the nerve centres in the physical body. The first is at the top of the head and the seventh at the base of the spine, with the five others coming in between – at the forehead, throat, heart, solar plexus and sacral region. The openings of the energy centres on the front of the body correspond with openings at the back. Both openings represent one and the same energy centre and the tips of the openings are at a distance of some inches from the body. The distance varies from person to person. The first energy centre, at the top of the head, and the seventh, at the base of the spine, are joined together vertically by an energy current and are sometimes considered as one.

The other five major energy centres run from front to back, and are joined into the main stream of energy which runs through the body. Each of these energy centres is associated with a particular sense: the sense of touch is associated with the first; hearing, smelling and tasting with the second, third and fourth, respectively; and seeing with the fifth. The tips of these five energy centres are joined at what are called the 'roots'. Within the roots are 'seals' which control the energy exchange between the seven layers of the human energy field or aura, which extends outside the physical body (see Chapter 3). The open end of each funnel-shaped energy centre is about six inches in diameter at a distance of about one inch from the body.

When the energy centres are working well, they are termed 'open'. They spin in a clockwise direction so as to utilise energy better. For overall good health – physical, mental, spiritual and emotional – it is necessary for all the energy centres to be open and balanced. A balance between the front and back of each energy centre is equally important, and if any of the centres need to be opened more, they must first be balanced with each other.

In the case of sick people, we have found that these energy centres are blocked. They may be clogged and torn, collapsed altogether or actually inverted. They may be spinning in an anticlockwise direction or the flow of energy into them may be erratic or one-sided. Whatever their condition, it is these blockages in the energy centres that have caused the illness. The more serious the blockage, the more serious the illness. The treatment involves reopening the centres so that the energy flow can be restored and balanced.

This reopening of the energy centres has to be done slowly and carefully over a number of therapy sessions, so as to allow the energy field time to adjust to the new state. If there is a blockage of energy, this may lead to physical illness; a blockage may also mean that the person is not in harmony with themselves or with those around them as a direct result of the imbalance. Such disharmony may have resulted from a prolonged illness and the psychic imprint left on the mind can sometimes take some time to remove.

People's energy centres vary according to their age, their level of maturity and their contentedness with life. As people grow and mature, it is normal for their energy centres to develop accordingly. But this is not always the case. For example, if a child is constantly rejected at a young age, eventually that child will have a heart energy centre that is underdeveloped. The energy flow to that centre will have been slowed down through the conscious will of the child as a result of the experience. A blocked heart energy centre has serious repercussions because it affects our capacity to love and to feel for other people around us. Similarly, if a person blocks off certain experiences, this means that the ability of the energy centre associated with that activity will be diminished.

In addition to their direct links to various organs and parts of the body, the energy centres are also associated with different psychological functions. The major energy centre at the base of the spine is linked to the quantity of physical energy a person possesses and the will to live. When this energy centre is working properly, a person will have a powerful will to live; when the centre is blocked, a person does not make a strong impression in the physical world and will generally avoid all physical activity. This centre is also responsible for sending energy to particular parts of the body (including the bones, blood, muscles, body tissues, adrenal glands, some internal and sex organs) and so it is a very important centre for a child's growth and development. If this energy centre is working badly, various illnesses can result, such as cancer, leukemia, arthritis, back pain, blood disorders, allergies and growth problems.

Working up from the base of the spine, the next energy centre is the sacral centre at the back and the pubic centre at the front. This centre is linked to sexual energy. Where the front and rear of this centre meet, at the roots, lies the desire for sexual union – one of the most powerful drives known to human beings. Any energy blockage in this region will have the effect of lowering a person's vitality for life. This centre also controls the bladder and can be adversely affected if either the throat, head or spinal centres are not working properly.

The solar plexus energy centre is related to the pleasure that comes from knowing oneself and one's place in the scheme of things, which in turn comes from a mental under-standing of the emotions. This centre has an important role to play in the control and ongoing health of the pancreas, liver, diaphragm, large intestine, appendix and lungs. It acts as a clearing house for the rest of the energy system since energies from the higher and lower energy centres all pass through here. If there is a lack of energy in a person's energy field, the entire body can be re-energised at this point. When the solar plexus centre is working well, a person will have a good emotional life that is orderly and regulated. A blockage here means that a person may be underdeveloped emotion-ally; on a physical level, this may manifest itself as diabetes, ulcers, hepatitis or heart disease. At the back, this energy centre is related to a person's desire for good physical health. When it is open, it indicates that a person has a strong desire to keep healthy. There is also a link between the solar plexus and the heart energy centres, since the former is sensitive to emotion and stress, evidenced by the fact that when people are involved in a stressful situation they feel a 'knot in the stomach'.

The heart energy centre controls the expression of love. The more open this centre, the more compassionate and caring the person. If it is closed, a person will experience difficulty in giving love without expecting anything in re-turn. This is the most important of all the centres in bio-en-ergy therapy. All energies circulating in the body, and which are utilised through the hands of the therapist, have to pass through this energy centre. Therefore what happens to the life energy at this point is very important.

Physically, the front of the heart energy centre controls the thymus gland and the circulation system. When it is not working properly, there may be heart and circulation-re-lated diseases. The solar plexus centre also has an effect on the heart centre: if there are problems in the former, they may also show up in the latter.

Between the shoulder blades is the back opening of the

heart energy centre. This relates to the will. If it is open and functioning normally, people have a good attitude about getting things done; if it is working badly, a negative attitude can be present, with the person seeing the world as basically a hostile place and the will of others in conflict with their own. This centre controls the lungs and to a lesser extent the heart. Problems here will show up as lung disorders. Putting energy into the back heart energy centre will help the heart. And again, the entire body can be energised from here.

The front throat energy centre relates to taking care of one's personal needs. As people mature, responsibility for seeing to their own needs rests with themselves. This manifests itself in not blaming others when things go wrong. A badly functioning energy centre here will mean that a person has a very low expectation of what people will do to help them when they are in trouble. The back throat centre relates to how people see themselves in society and within their profession or trade. If the centre is working well, it means that the person is satisfied with their work and fairly contented; if the centre is blocked or not working properly, the person will feel unfulfilled and will not give of their best. On the physical level, the throat centre controls the thyroid and parathyroid glands and is related to disorders such as goitre, sore throat, asthma and loss of voice.

The front forehead energy centre relates to the understanding of concepts and the creative instinct. If this centre is not working properly, it is likely that the person will have a confused picture of reality and how the world works. At the back, the centre deals with the ability to implement the creative ideas thought of at the front; if the centre is open, ideas will be followed through by action. Physically, the forehead energy centre controls the pineal gland and the nervous system, as well as the pituitary and endocrine glands and various other vital organs. Disorders such as loss of memory, paralysis and epilepsy can result if this centre is blocked or malfunctioning. Hence, this centre has a great influence over all the other major energy centres. The entire energy system can be energised from here very quickly.

The energy centre on the crown of the head is related to the whole health of the person – spiritually, emotionally, mentally and physically. A closed centre will mean that a person can have great difficulty in relating to spiritual matters; this is not to suggest a spirituality related to any type of organised religion, but more to do with a person's sense of contentment and purpose. Physically, this centre controls the pineal gland, the brain – in fact, the entire body.

THE DETECTION OF ENERGY IMBALANCES

There are various ways to find out if the energy centres are blocked or malfunctioning. The main way we work is to sense these centres through our hands. When we scan the energy field of a patient using our hands, we can read the interaction of their energy and our energy through our fingers and palms. It is possible to tell by feel alone whether the energy is flowing freely or whether it is blocked. Every bio-energy therapist monitors the response in their hands differently. When we diagnose what is wrong with a person on an energy level, we pass our hands along the energy centres, both back and front. We keep our hands as close to the body as possible without actually touching it. We can then feel the excess of energy as a heat and a tingling flowing through our outstretched fingers. The only analogy we can make is to compare the feeling to sand running through one's fingers.

We can feel the energy going into the energy centres. If the energy is flowing correctly, in a clockwise direction, then all is well and no corrective action is necessary. If, however, the energy is flowing in an anticlockwise direction, we then know the centre is closed. Again, we are able to tell this by the way the energy going in responds to our hands. A patient we are treating in this way could feel a number of things at this point: they might feel a heat or a tingling or a strong pull in the direction of our hands. The larger the vortex through which the energy enters, the greater will be the energy centre itself and the greater the amount of energy that flows in to it. A comparison must be made between all the various energy centres in order to ensure they are in balance with each other. If one is out of balance, sweeping motions must be made so as to balance it with the others. In this way, the body's entire energy field is balanced.

The more distorted the clockwise movement of energy into a particular centre, the more of a problem the patient has. The speed with which the energy enters is also a good indicator: a fast-moving energy flow means that energy is being processed quickly through that particular centre, while a slow-moving energy flow indicates slow processing. The more experienced we have become as therapists, the better we are able to interpret the variations of energy entering the centres and therefore the more accurate the diagnosis of a patient's problems on an energy level. With treatment, the energy centres will eventually stabilise and be restored to their original condition. The more work that is done on a patient over a period of time, the better. We often call patients back to our clinics in order to assess their energy levels over a period of time and to monitor their progress.

Sometimes the therapy can have an immediate effect, with some patients needing only five minutes of treatment for their energy to be put in balance. Each patient is different and there is no hard and fast rule about this. Bio-energy therapy is a highly personalised form of helping people. As well as understanding this for ourselves, we have been told as much by our patients: many who attend our clinics have complained of the depersonalised nature of the treatment they have received from conventional medicine.

Bio-energy has much to offer conventional medicine. The therapy has the potential to provide information that cannot be revealed through the traditional forms of diagnosis, which often involve fitting a given set of symptoms into a predetermined disease frame. The application of bio-energy therapy can identify a disease or a condition at an energy level before it manifests itself in the physical body. It is our belief that in the future medical science will utilise bio-energy therapy to detect physical diseases before they show up in the body and preventative medicine will take a giant step forward. The therapy can also speed up the healing process following surgery or an accident and this, in turn, will allow the patient to regain their health more quickly. In addition, the therapy offers a much broader view of what causes illness in the first place.

THE NATURE OF ILLNESS

The first thing that must be said is that disease is perfectly natural, something that is part and parcel of being alive. But nowhere is it written that people must continue to suffer from various conditions for prolonged periods of time. When energy is flowing freely through the energy centres to the various parts of the body, the risk of disease and sickness is reduced. If the energy centres are blocked, an imbalance of the energy field will follow and this in turn will lead to a chemical disturbance in the body which will manifest itself as an illness sooner or later if it is not rectified.

The relationship between human beings and nature lies at the heart of bio-energy therapy. Established medicine has long ago restricted itself in the understanding of this point. When a person's health is viewed strictly in terms of the physical body, there is little thought given to other causative factors outside the strictly physical domain. One example of this is the fact that only in recent decades has psychiatric illness been recognised as such; up to then, if an illness did not have a physical manifestation, it was deemed not to exist. Thus, medical science at last recognised that although a person might be physically well, there could be illness at an emotional or mental level which could leave the physical body open to disease if the condition were not dealt with.

The recognition of mental disease has a further significance in so far as human beings get diseases that are unknown in the animal or plant world. One way of viewing these diseases is to consider the body as the stage on which all the drama takes place. In reality, however, there is much more happening behind the scenes. Any treatment which would hope to make a person well has to take this into account.

Negative attitudes and emotional stresses in an individual have the effect of weakening the immunity system and causing blockages and depletions of energy which, in turn, can leave the body open to disease. Stress is a particularly good example of this. It is a product of the age we live in and has become the greatest curse of the late twentieth century. Energy blockages are particularly noticeable in the energy fields of a patient suffering from stress. When people are under pressure, their body reacts in a predetermined way. The first reaction is alarm, followed by the secretion of adrenalin to face the stress. If the stress continues, the next response is to try and adapt to the stress, which uses up a great deal of energy that might be used in other ways. With continued stress, the final reaction is for the physical body to try and contain the stress – damage limitation, so to speak. The body's energy is so depleted at this stage that immunity has been lowered and disease is likely to set in.

In order to understand the nature of bio-energy and how it helps people to heal themselves, it is first necessary to understand the nature of the disease, no matter how serious it is. This understanding is the key to re-establishing the psychological balance of the individual and their energy field. Once this harmonisation is achieved, the individual holds the key to their future health. In order to get to this stage, we have to look at all the various aspects that go to make up the individual and how each of these aspects can affect harmony and health.

There are many things that are important – what we eat,

where we live and a sense of purpose in our lives. While health problems can be eliminated with bio-energy therapy in the short term, it is vital that the underlying cause of the problem is dealt with; otherwise, the same disorder, or even another, will soon manifest itself again due to a recurrence of energy imbalance. We take the view that energy imbalance, which can be caused by a number of factors, is the root of many physical illnesses and conditions. A positive attitude towards life, combined with harmonious relationships and thinking, helps in overall good health. It is not easy for people to reach this point and there is no written 'code of harmony' to consult for guidance; what is harmony for one person could be discord for another.

One of the main reasons that people today have problems in achieving this harmony is that we are faced with many modern handicaps. There is an ascending hierarchy of needs and desires which has been identified by psychologists as the way in which human beings act and develop. At a very basic level, our needs are simple: all we require is food, clothing and shelter. Once we have these things, we start to make other demands on life which are more difficult to meet. Thus, we begin to direct our efforts to objectives and desires that have little to do with our basic survival. The pinnacle of our desires is reached when we begin to use our intelligence in a creative way. This has the effect of fulfilling internal drives and the scope for personal development is limitless, or rather it is limited only by our own imagination.

These needs within us have to be married to the way we live in the modern world. But the very type of affluence which allows us to develop in this way and to reach our full potential is also a hindrance in other ways. Modern technology has given us the freedom to pursue our desires but the same technology has also removed us from nature. We are more in tune today with machines and technology than with nature. Life in the modern world does not lend itself to a process whereby we can fulfill ourselves and at the same time stay close to our roots. We believe that this quandary has much to do with our inability to achieve harmony in our lives.

We are not saying that bio-energy therapy is the total answer to this seemingly insurmountable problem. What we are saying, however, is that this therapy can be part of the groundwork that it is necessary to lay before there is a reconciliation, or harmonisation, between modern technology and nature. If someone has benefitted from bio-energy therapy and then insists upon returning to the same stresses and contradictions that caused the problem in the first place, then it is to be expected that the disorder will reoccur. The harmonious balance achieved as a result of the therapy will be disrupted and the whole process, while it could not be called a complete waste of time, will have been negated.

People need to look at their entire lifestyle and values in order to understand the underlying cause of their problem, not just the physical symptoms. Obviously, this is not the case with, say, car-accident victims. The sort of illnesses we are talking about here are ones which have persisted for a long time despite the best efforts of conventional medicine. They are problems with no apparent cause. But patients sometimes have to go back over their lives to pinpoint the start of the problem and the trigger that caused it. Only then will the therapy be truly successful in the long term.

A CODE FOR LIVING

What we need is a code for living. This is not intended to be like a religious code or in any way dogmatic. The best way of explaining what we mean is to say that the code we are talking about is one which people are comfortable with and which helps them in their lives. To suggest that people have a code to live by after attending a bio-energy clinic is not as strange as it might sound. After all, even in conventional medical science, various codes have played, and continue to play, an important part in the ongoing treatment of people.

When doctors are trying to help heart patients, for example, part of the code of behaviour involves a strict diet for the patient. But the alternative code we are talking about will involve people taking a look at the way they have been treated by established medicine. We need to examine how we have handed responsibility for our own health over to others.

In the modern world, we enjoy a technical superiority undreamt of by previous generations. This has led us to the belief that our health is something outside of ourselves, something over which we have little control. When we get ill and visit the doctor, we expect to be given a pill to cure whatever is wrong with us. The idea is continually reinforced that when we get sick it is somebody else who will hand us the cure. We rarely look inside ourselves for the answer. But even if we do come to realise that we should be taking more responsibility for our health, it is probably too late and we are not in a position to help ourselves. We are probably too ill to challenge anything and we think we have no other choice but to place our faith in others so that we can get well. We have got to realise that the road to good health is in our own hands.

Another complicating factor when we fall ill is that we tend to blame other things outside of ourselves for our condition. This attitude gets around any responsibility we might have for our own health and omits the crucial aspect of personal involvement in the healing process. This attitude can, in turn, engender fear, resentment, lack of initiative and self-confidence, all of which could be considered disorders in themselves and which sometimes need as much treatment as a physical disorder. These are attitudes which we could well do without if we really want to be healthy. And this is an area which has been, by and large, neglected by the established medical profession.

In this modern age, awareness of physical hygiene and health has been brought to new heights. The importance of maintaining a mental balance, while not being totally neglected, has been relegated to a poor second. Part of the reason for this might be explained in terms of expanding materialism. When material success does not bring the expected contentment, this can cause stress along with a feeling of emptiness. The only way this feeling can be staved off is by acquiring more material possessions, and so on. This attitude does not tackle the underlying problem in our lives, whatever that problem might be: it just hides it for a while. But the picture is not totally bleak. There are many signs today that we have come to realise our removal from nature is not a good thing and many people are taking tentative steps towards living in harmony with the natural world.

The beginning of this change of heart is best seen in the many ecological movements that have sprung up around the world. There is now a global awareness that we must take care of our environment. For perhaps the first time in human history, we are coming to realise the real meaning of the 'one planet' theory – that pollution knows no national boundaries and it will affect all living things, including the human race. Collective responsibility is the only way that this problem can be tackled effectively. But underlying all of this concern is the idea that we should have respect for nature which heals us and protects us from disease. Inherent in this is the belief that action must be taken sooner rather than later.

Another point worth making in relation to our modern lifestyle is that it has become less and less natural during this century. We have synthetic clothing, additives in food, chemicals and electromagnetic waves and perhaps other things which we are not even aware of (see Chapter 4) creating havoc with our health. On the other hand, people who are healthy give considerable thought to how they live their lives and incorporate a responsible attitude towards everything that they do. This attitude is different for everyone, but one aspect of living that can have an immediate effect on our lives is what we eat. Our modern diet contains many chemicals not found naturally in the body; grains and wheats, which used to be the mainstay of our diet, have slowly disappeared in favour of meats. Increasingly, dieticians and nutritionists have begun to recognise that a balanced diet is important in the prevention of disease. They recommend more natural foodstuffs – cereals, beans, fresh fruit and vegetables – in order to reduce the risk of serious ailments. We are not qualified dieticians and this is not the place to outline a healthy diet; there are enough reputable books available on the subject. Healthy eating is largely a matter of common sense in any event. Unhealthy eating will eventually give rise to an unhealthy body and mind, and this state of affairs will sooner or later show up at an energy level, both inside and outside the body.

HEALING

Emotions play a major part in healing. They can block or impair the whole process. If we were to deal only with the physical problems of a condition, we would be making a serious omission in the treatment of our patients. When a patient is undergoing bio-energy therapy, they are neither an object of science nor a mere energy field. We treat all patients as human beings and each patient is special. This can be a very different approach to what most people have come to expect.

The treatment itself differs from established medicine in that it is not exclusively concerned with the laws that govern the physical world. We are dealing with energy, something which we can feel and manipulate but which cannot be explained in scientific terms. To date, scientific testing of the therapy has concerned itself with trying to find out the exact pathway through which energy is transferred either from or to the patient. One of the more interesting theories regards the universe as being holographic. What this means is that one part of the universe is capable of containing within itself a technical blueprint for the reproduction of the whole. This implies that each tiny part of the universe is linked to every other part. When scientists then look for a means whereby energy can be transferred through the therapist to the patient, or a pathway through which energy is conducted, it may be that they are looking in vain, because if the universe is holographic and everything is connected, then there need not be anything at all through which the energy is conducted. If this theory is correct, it means that the all-present energies, together with all their manifestations (such as brain impulses, electromagnetic waves, gravity fields and electricity), are only part of a larger picture – the nuts and bolts of the energy process that are to be found at the very bottom rung of the energy ladder.

Regardless of what the theories say, the initial treatment with bio-energy therapy is the active ingredient which starts off the healing process. The vital healing is done by the patient himself or herself and it takes place on the basis that we have established a rapport with the patient on an energy level. Both ourselves and the patient actively participate in the healing in this sense, but the results that are achieved are due to the patient's own inherent ability to heal himself.

Healthy people have the ability to heal themselves. But when energy gets blocked, then this ability is diminished. There are many different things that can cause this inability to develop, among them attitudes, negative thoughts or trauma. One of the most important things for us when we are treating people is to rise above the thought that it is impossible to help our patients, no matter what disease or condition they are suffering from. Everybody, including ourselves, has been conditioned to think of certain conditions as incurable and terminal. These limitations have to be overcome in order to carry out the therapy successfully and we have genuinely to believe that any and every condition can be successfully treated with bio-energy therapy.

WHO CAN DO BIO-ENERGY THERAPY?

The ability to help people using bio-energy therapy is one which everyone has within themselves. It is an ability which can be developed and trained. It is not a new therapy: many Eastern cultures have left records and drawings which show healers curing people by the laying-on of hands or other similar methods. What these documents do not show is the necessary state of mind of the person who is carrying out the curing. In our therapy, our psychological state when we are working is crucial. The movements we use to release blocked energy or to add energy are really only a form: it is our intention that is important – in fact, it is everything.

It is not necessary that we have formal qualifications or letters after our names in order to recognise the possibilities in our own hands. The main thing we have to recognise is that there exists a vital life force that surrounds us all the time, that we are a part of it and that we can utilise it to help people who are unwell. We also know that no amount of theory gives an insight into the results that have been ob-tained using the therapy both in Yugoslavia by Domancic and in Ireland by ourselves. What we have found is that the intensity and quality of the treatment is in direct proportion to our desire to help people and that we have to look beyond the disease or condition and look instead at the individual being treated.

There are other factors which must be taken into account. The healing process can only be undertaken by a completely healthy person. If we are unwell ourselves, we will not attempt to treat a patient. The reason for this is that a sick person trying to help another sick person will not necessarily be successful and it is possible to do more harm than good in that state. We have also found that the presence of people not emotionally linked to the patient is not a good idea while treatment is going on. Nor is the presence of people who are negative towards the therapy. Such people can affect the outcome, since negativity can be picked up on an energy level and we are dealing with subtle energies.

Although there have sometimes been spectacular results using the therapy, there have been problems with monitoring and measuring exactly what has happened. One of the main problems with objective scientific attempts is that the treatment is, in fact, very subjective. It is just not possible to objectify that which is subjective and therefore to measure it. We can illustrate this with an example. When a person who is unwell goes to their doctor, the doctor asks them where they have pain and then collates a set of symptoms which fits the disorder into a known category. The doctor may then prescribe medication and after a while the pain and the symptoms may disappear. All the evidence for the 'curing' comes from the patient because it is the patient who tells the doctor that they are unwell and then that they are better.

With bio-energy therapy, attempts have been made to measure this process whereby people go from sickness to health, not by asking the patient but by measuring it with instruments. This standard is not used by doctors to validate their results. In our opinion, the inner world of human beings and what they experience cannot be made so objective as to be measured down to the last detail.

As far as the healing process is concerned, determining the energy imbalances and directing the healing energies is done exclusively by the healer. In carrying out the therapy, the initial diagnosis on an energy level is important. The exact locations where blockages need to be released and healing energy put in have to be found. We are trained to spot the energy imbalances and to know how they can be rectified. This is done mainly through changes in the temperature of our hands as they travel over the patient's energy field. This knowledge is largely intuitive and we instinctively know what is wrong and where. The feelings in our hands can vary from warm to hot to cold to ice cold to tingling sensations. The patient may also feel similar sensations, but it is not important to the therapy for him to feel anything. We have had many cases where people have recovered from their illness and have felt little or nothing when the therapy was being carried out.

The length of time a patient is treated depends on the illness itself and how long the healing process takes. With some people, five minutes may be enough, while with others months of treatment may be necessary before they are well again. In a four- or five-day clinic, there will be changes in a patient's energy field and the balance has to be continually restored until the field is able to adjust itself. If the reactions of the treatment on either the patient or ourselves are very powerful, then we usually stop the treatment for that day.

The human energy field or aura is a subtle imprint around the physical body. It is an energy image of the body itself and contains our complete genetic make-up. In bio-energy therapy, if the patient and the therapist are on the same frequency, as it were, it makes a great difference to the potential results and the process of the patient healing himself is made that much easier. In addition, the energy field will change under emotional and mental pressures and this can be felt by a trained therapist. These changes can be picked up in other ways, too. In Kirlian photography, for example, the body's luminosity contacts a high-frequency electrical field and changes can be noted in it through the physical and mental changes taking place in the person. Just as an X-ray shows the condition of the bones and internal organs, Kirlian photography shows the bio-energy condition of the human energy field.

CHAPTER 3

The Energy Field Explored

❁

DIVORCE FROM NATURE

We can all remember times when we have been so depressed that we were unable to do anything and no amount of will or effort could pull us out of it. Then again, there are times when we get a tremendous surge of energy and we feel we could 'take on the world'. People cannot explain this surge of energy or where it comes from. All we know is that we are in touch with ourselves and that all is well. In order to understand about energy, we need to explore why these two states come about, and in particular how illness occurs.

When someone is suffering from a prolonged illness, they are generally unable to help themselves get better. The process that has made them ill can often be a long and harrowing one (although sometimes it can be quite sudden, as in the case of a car or sporting accident). Many factors play a part in wearing down people's resistance, so that they feel there is no hope. They tend to see little meaning in their lives; in some cases, there is constant pain and it is often hard to see beyond this, especially if the person has explored all the avenues of conventional medicine. The one ingredient that might change this state of affairs – hope – is gradually eroded. Only someone who has suffered such a prolonged illness, or who has watched someone close to them suffer, can fully appreciate how one can be brought to the edge of the abyss.

ENERGY AND A SENSE OF PURPOSE

Constant illness saps a person's energy and they begin to

feel that they have no control over the situation. To a certain extent, this is true but it is not the full picture. In an ideal world, ill people could utilise other factors to ensure that life did not look so bleak, thereby bringing meaning back into their lives which is the first step on the road to recovery.

Ill people do not, however, live in an ideal world. A number of problems have to be overcome before they can regain a sense of purpose in their lives and get the energy to do something about their situation. One of the main ways of achieving this is to be active and to have a specific purpose in being active. This might seem impossible for someone who has been ill for a long time and whose will has been greatly diminished by pain and suffering. Indeed, it is extremely difficult for a sick person to do this on their own since they rarely have an insight into how their mental state has been affected by their physical illness. They must be helped by those in a position to do so.

There is a supreme irony here, as we approach the end of the twentieth century. In this modern age, with apparently every convenience and drug available to medical science, many sick people cannot be cured. It is also ironic that the average lifespan in the Western world has not changed all that much in the last few decades. We would say that our modern world, which has given us so much, may actually be part of the problem in relation to illness rather than part of the cure. This is not to say that modern medicine has not achieved great things: many diseases and plagues have been largely beaten, such as TB and smallpox, and spectacular advances have been made in such fields as neurosurgery and organ transplantation. But in order to understand why our lives, in general, have not greatly changed in relation to illness, we have to look at the way we live today and compare this with the way our ancestors lived. In our opinion, many of the changes that are apparent in the modern world have not always been for the better. There are various stresses associated with modern living which many people are not even aware of – stresses which our grandparents and great-grandparents never experienced. Our lives are structured very differently to those of people a few centuries ago. We no longer, for example, have to hunt for our food or even grow it. Most of us have food, shelter and clothing beyond our needs.

As we have taken this direction in our lives something else has happened to us, something so basic and fundamental that we are not even aware of it. Our modern way of living has divorced us from nature in a way that our predecessors could not have imagined. This process has happened quite quickly and there have been few attempts to quantify the effects on our psyche.

Having all our basic survival needs supplied has made us into spectators of our own lives. We are less active participants in every respect and more prepared to accept whatever happens to us. If we had to depend on our own ability to feed and fend for ourselves, we would have a feeling of physical control over our lives, like our ancestors did. But this feeling is clearly missing from much of modern living. (Of course, some people do manage to gain a position of authority in which they exercise effective control over their own lives, but such people are a minority.)

What has happened as a result of our divorce from nature is that we are no longer in tune with the life energy. Our overall vitality has decreased; it is further diminished when we are ill, to a point where we cannot revive it by our own efforts. Let us take a closer look at the ways in which we can lose vitality and the repercussions this has on our health. Having a harmony and balance in our lives keeps us healthy. We feel at one with ourselves and with those around us. In this state, we are – whether we realise it or not – utilising the life energy to our best advantage. When we lose our sense of vitality, we can also lose or lessen our sense of purpose. Then we begin to function on a purely automatic level, going through each day in a robot-like state, with nothing new or fresh in our lives and unable to drum up any enthusiasm.

We have noticed this listlessness in the initial stages of treating many sick people. They think there is no further challenge for their mental, physical and creative abilities, and they have come to accept this state as normal, probably because they have been like that for a long time. We are not, of course, saying that people who fall ill are responsible for their own condition or for the gradual erosion of their will. This process is almost inevitable and there is little they can do to restore their confidence and energy once the cycle starts. Their energy for life wanes and, again, this is not their fault. This lessening of energy is a progressive thing and can lead to the point where sick people fully accept their illness and believe they can do nothing about it. What we are witnessing in such cases are sick people waiting for life to offer them a 'quick fix'. They live with the unrealistic expectation that a solution will be offered to their problems. Several factors may have led to this, among them the conditioning they have received from both the medical profession and the church. But life has no quick solutions and the answer to most problems lies within people themselves. Part of the healing process involves learning and believing this. We have been able to instill in people during bio-energy therapy sessions a sense of their own self-worth and recognition of their own ability to heal themselves.

While we do not enjoy dwelling on this aspect, in order to understand bio-energy therapy we must elaborate somewhat on the progressive decline experienced during the phases of prolonged illness. A sick person's mental state of hopelessness usually gets increasingly worse and life becomes bleaker. At a certain point, they will come to the view that they are trapped, that there is no way out for them, and the essence of freedom – choice – appears to them no longer available. Many sick people can become bitter and selfish at this point and their attitude towards most things is negative. But they are not yet at the bottom of the abyss.

Relatives and friends notice the change in mental attitude, but there never appears to be anything they can do about it; telling people to 'pull themselves together' just does not work. By now, the most important thing for the therapist to treat is not the person's original illness but their current frame of mind. If this is not successfully tackled, every other form of treatment may be a waste of time. In our experience, turning around this negative attitude usually requires a great deal of effort, but the importance of doing so cannot be overstated.

The final level a sick person can reach is one in which it is extremely hard to motivate them to do anything, since they believe that nothing is worth the effort. They can become self-centred to the exclusion of everything else. In combination with their sense of boredom, life takes on a sort of nightmarish quality which is very hard to describe or appreciate if one has not been through it.

Sick people can develop all kinds of irrational fears during their waking hours which gradually take over their lives. Such secret fears may range from a belief that somebody is set on harming them or stealing from them to simply a fear of fear itself. We have come across many cases of sick people living like this and often, in our opinion, their state of health was not helped by the medication they were taking at the time. They may find it hard to sleep and this can be partly due to the drugs themselves. We have found in our clinics that a lack of sleep in a patient suffering a prolonged illness further erodes their will and physical strength.

We have been describing very sick people here – not people with a cold or 'flu who suffer for a few days and then are better again. We are talking about people who have been sick for years, in some cases decades. But anyone who has had a bad dose of a 'flu that rendered them powerless even for a few days will have an insight into the loss of vitality described above.

Apart altogether from the illness itself, there are other

factors involved which affect a person. One of these is conventional medicine. We have regrettably come to the view, as a result of working with many cases, that established medicine can play a part in eroding the will of sick people. This is related to people's expectations, especially their unfulfilled expectations. They are led to believe that when they fall ill, all they have to do is to attend a doctor, or perhaps a specialist, get some medication and then they will be better again. This view of the world, where everything will be taken care of, promotes the idea that people's health is something outside themselves, something which can be dealt with in isolation from the rest of their lives. This is a most dangerous concept, since it means that people have as good as handed over responsibility for their health to a science which may let them down. We know that many have been let down because they come to our bio-energy clinics having inevitably been somebody else's patient first. At this point, let us make it quite clear that we believe that many people are helped by conventional medicine and that it has much to offer.

In order to appreciate how the failure of conventional medicine can effect a state of hopelessness in people, let us take a brief look at how the medical faculty views the world, in particular the world of sick people. Our views on this have been formed over the years as a result of talking to thousands of sick people and listening to their stories about how they have been treated.

Conventional medicine concerns itself with the physical world almost exclusively. When people get sick, they feel trapped in this physical reality which has been created for them. In general, sick people do not think that anything outside their physical body or outside what they can experience with their senses can have a real effect on their condition. (There are exceptions to this, of course, with hundreds of thousands of people going to Knock or Lourdes each year in the hope of getting a cure, but the percentage of miracles that occurs is small.) The central point – that sick people think that the only aspects of their lives over which they can have a direct control involves their physical reality alone – still holds true.

By and large, it is true to say that the practitioners of established medicine do not take account of the fact that we interact with the world and living things on an energy level as well as on a physical level. Conventional medicine has broken the world into component parts and it holds the view that the sum total of these parts constitutes the entirety of the human being. People are therefore viewed as a sum total of biological parts in which a series of chemical actions and reactions takes place.

These are extremely limited terms of reference, but they are the reason why science holds to the belief that the earth and everything in it is explicable only in its own terms. Science in general does not believe that there is more than one way of looking at the world. This assertion is patently absurd and arrogant. The conventional scientific view of the world reduces everything to an objective level. This objectivity is necessary, it is said, in order to validate certain things. Nothing could be further from the truth. In fact, anything that the scientific community cannot explain, does not understand or cannot measure by its own yardsticks is usually ignored or rejected. Many phenomena never get examined because certain members of the scientific community do not think they are worthwhile.

It is only in the last hundred years or so that medical science has claimed to have a monopoly on health and on the care of sick people. Long before medical doctors were ever heard of, people had their own way of dealing with illness by natural methods which involved being close to and in tune with nature. The fact that two types of energy (earth energy and cosmic energy) were used by priests and other respected individuals in ancient civilisations has been effectively rejected by mainstream scientists in recent centuries. But science has been proved wrong before. One of the earliest examples of scientific dogma that was elevated to the status of a belief was the theory that the earth was flat and that the universe revolved around the earth. This view was held for hundreds of years and those who sought to challenge it were not treated kindly. What is held to be true in one century can be held to be utter rubbish in the next. Isaac Newton, the discoverer of gravity and the high priest of modern science, for example, would have been astounded at the fact that electromagnetic waves are used to send radio signals across the earth today; he would probably not have believed in their existence.

Ancient civilisations believed that the energies of the earth and cosmos were directly involved with the generative and regenerative forces of nature. Nature was treated as a total living organism and people considered themselves part of the scheme of things. This closeness to nature led to a constant awareness of not only the physical reality of life, but also another, deeper, hidden reality. People viewed nature as a facade behind which there was an even greater drama taking place. This awareness meant that nature was respected and treated as a living entity. In order to survive and be healthy and happy, people had to be in harmony with nature and develop an understanding of the earth's forces and powers. What we view nowadays as their religious services could be considered, by and large, as an interaction between nature's energies and their own.

In contrast to this, there are so many distractions in the modern world that we have forgotten that these energies exist and that they can influence us in many different ways, including our health. It is only in recent decades that we have begun to look again at what our ancestors believed and how they used these energies.

MODERN SCIENCE

There is evidence that ancient civilisations were aware of

the fact that the earth has its own magnetic lines and that it is possible at special intersections on the surface to tap into the earth's energies and use them for various purposes. Many ancient monuments were built at sites where the earth's magnetic lines are strongest and hence where the concentrations of energies are more powerful than those found in the immediate surroundings.

The surface of the earth has identifiable lines of magnetic force and the earth itself is influenced by other heavenly bodies. The moon, in particular, influences the earth – the tides, for example, are controlled by the phases of the moon. It is also a fact that during the lunar cycle, the behaviour of certain people suffering from psychiatric disorders is affected. Hospitals and police departments the world over are only too aware that psychiatric disturbances and the crime rate, respectively, are more pronounced at full moon.

Thus, the interaction of the universe's energies can have an influence on human behaviour. Dowsers are a good example of this. They have the gift of being able to locate water underground, among other things, by using rods, twigs, a pendulum or simply their hands. It is a well-recorded fact that some dowsers feel faint when they are working; this indicates that their own energies are interacting with those of the earth's forces to which they are particularly sensitive. Many scientists do not take the art of the dowser seriously, but others have attempted to quantify and monitor it.

The view that we are all just so many biological parts and little else is being increasingly questioned, even by the scientific community itself. The results of some experiments go against accepted scientific laws, which is giving some scientists, at least, food for thought. In one series of experiments, the behaviour of fertilized embryos suggests that even when half the cells have been destroyed, the other half will produce a whole specimen. A living organism thus aims at a sort of oneness or completeness. This being the case, it follows that the biological process is not just purely automatic and biological because, if it was, then the behaviour of the embryo would be quite different. This means that there is a part of the organism which has a vital purpose separate from the purely biological function that science would have us ascribe to it. There is something here to suggest that we are more than just flesh and bones, something which should be investigated deeply and which in time may change the way we look at life.

The purely biological view of the human body put forward by most doctors and scientists is, in our opinion, the greatest stumbling block for people who fall ill. We view illness as due to an energy imbalance. Some people are still in touch with nature, so they will be able automatically to tune in and rebalance their own energies. But most people cannot do this because they have lost touch with their roots.

Many people who come to us for bio-energy therapy have gone through all the various phases of illness. The first phase involves pain. This, in turn, can lead to fear, which can lead to guilt in the case of some people who think their suffering is an atonement for some past wrong, an attitude that further diminishes their will to get better. The church, incidentally, is not very helpful in this regard. Many people still believe that the church teaches that they must suffer pain and that by enduring it they will be rewarded in the next life. They are taught that there is an inevitability about this and that to try and rid oneself of suffering is somehow to go against the will of the Creator. The fostering of this attitude is wrong, counter-productive and narrow-minded. Such negative thinking can make people even more depressed about their condition. They feel isolated and cannot summon up the energy to do anything. The final phase is almost total inertia and hopelessness, with the illness becoming the focal point of their existence.

A POSITIVE APPROACH

Sick people need to be taught a positive approach to their problems. They do not need to be told that there is no hope. Nowhere is it written that people have to be sick or that their destiny is to suffer. Many cancer patients who have been unsuccessfully treated by medical science are told that there is nothing more that can be done for them. Some are given a short time to live. This is a death sentence by another name. We have come across many cases where this sentence has been imprinted on the mind of a patient – and the prophecy can be self-fulfilling.

If a patient recovers from a terminal illness, this is classified as either a miracle or, in medical terms, a 'spontaneous remission'. We have come across enough cases of people sent home to die to be able to say a few things about their condition. In such cases, the people have ceased to evolve and are no longer following their natural instincts, which in normal circumstances maintain health. Their minds are slowed down to the point where they refuse to take responsibility for their own health. They have been forced to a standstill, an attitude that inevitably engenders further illness. Their vital energies are gone as well as their will.

Turning this negative attitude around is not to give people a false hope. It is a hope based on the reality that it is within everyone's power to heal themselves using their own inherent abilities. We have seen numerous cases where sick people have recovered and have begun to look at life in a new and different way.

THE ENERGY FIELD OR AURA

Each and every one of us has an energy field or 'aura' – we are born with it. People imagine it to be made up of a brightly coloured series of layers surrounding the body, and for those lucky enough to be able to see it, this is indeed how it looks. In the course of our work, we explain to people about their individual aura and how it works. But we do not ask them to accept this on trust; there is a sound scientific basis for it, investigated by some forward-thinking scientists who, sadly, are considered mavericks by their own profession.

The fact that the human energy field exists has been known for centuries. Many world religions talk of 'light' emanating from around the heads of people who have reached a high degree of spiritual attainment. In such 'holy' people, the aura is said to be of the purest white or even gold. This is not unique to the Christian tradition. In India more than 5000 years ago, this light or energy was called 'prana'. The Chinese called it 'Ch'i' and believed that all matter was composed of it. The book of the Jewish religion, the *Kabbalah*, refers to 'astral light'. In the Western world, the first writers to mention the aura were the Greek Pythagoreans, around 500 years before Christ. They said that the light around people could have different effects on other people and that the light could be used to cure illness.

SCIENCE INVESTIGATES THE AURA

Science has been using machines to measure energy for years. For example, electrical energy from the heart is measured with an electrocardiogram (ECG), while energy from the brain is measured with an electroencephalogram (EEG). Lie detectors measure energy on the skin.

Attempts to measure the 'dynamic energy' of the human energy field or aura have met with varying degrees of success. One such device, called the Superconducting Quantum Interference Device (SQUID), actually gives more information about the brain than the EEG does. In the mid-1800s, Count Wilhelm von Reichenback spent 30 years investigating what he called the 'odic force'; he believed that the greatest concentration of this force lay in the red and blue-violet ranges of the colour spectrum. (In general, this end of the spectrum is invisible to the human eye, although some people have trained themselves to see this range of colours and can therefore see the human aura.) Naturally enough,

Reichenback received the usual sceptical reaction from his colleagues. Around the same time, Dr Wilhelm Reich, a colleague of Sigmund Freud, was investigating the universal energy or 'orgon', and he noted the correlation between a person's energy field and their state of health.

Over the decades, researchers have come to accept that this energy field surrounding the human body can be put to medical use and is crucial to good health. When the aura is healthy so is the body, and vice versa. For example, in 1911 Dr Walter Kilner of St Thomas's Hospital in London reported, after years of watching the aura through coloured screens, that it was made up of several layers which differed according to the sex, age, mental ability and health of the individual. He was able to correlate what he could see outside the body with what was happening to the body itself and he noted that certain diseases manifested themselves as patches in the aura. He recognised the potential of using this knowledge as a diagnostic tool to help sick people.

In 1936, Semyon and Valentine Kirlian, the Soviet husband and wife team, photographed what they called 'bioplasmic' energy. Using a high-frequency generator and normal photographic paper, they reproduced images of the human aura that looked like sparks, strongest at the outside of the subject and appearing in certain patterns towards the inside. This was the first scientific proof that all living things were surrounded by a complex electronic field. The Kirlians' work was highly controversial and other scientists greeted their results as merely 'spectacular photographs'.

Then, in 1959, Dr Leonard Ravitz of William and Mary University in the USA showed that the aura changed according to a person's mental and physiological health. He went so far as to suggest that there was an electronic field directly associated with the thought process. The implications of this theory are enormous, since it admits that sick people can actually have an effect on their own illness and that other people can also exert an influence on them.

Michael O'Doherty treating young Mathew Lowe as he is held by his mother. Blockages of energy, which can and do lead to a problem in the physical body, are released by a 'drawing away' motion from the patient, as in this picture. The patient may feel a heat or a tingling sensation whilst this is going on.

Bio-energy Therapists Michael O'Doherty and Tom Griffin. They studied bio-energy therapy under Zdenko Domancic in Yugoslavia, and worked for five years to popularise the therapy in Ireland. They developed their knowledge, and have recently started large scale clinics in England. They were invited back by the Yugoslavs to open clinics and to demonstrate their knowledge.

Above: A view from the back of a typical bio-energy clinic. At the top of the hall, various therapists, including Michael O'Doherty and Tom Griffin, are at different stages of treating their patients. Other patients, who have yet to be treated, wait.

Left: Tom Griffin and Tina Griffin 'tune in' to the energy fields of their patients. This process is necessary before a diagnosis of an energy level can be made.

This is how the energy field should look when the person is 100 per cent healthy. This health is reflected at a physical, mental, emotional, spiritual and astral level. The person is in complete harmony and balance with their surroundings and with those with whom they come in contact. This is the ideal situation. If that person had problems on any level, the energy field would be distorted in some way and the colours would be clouded.

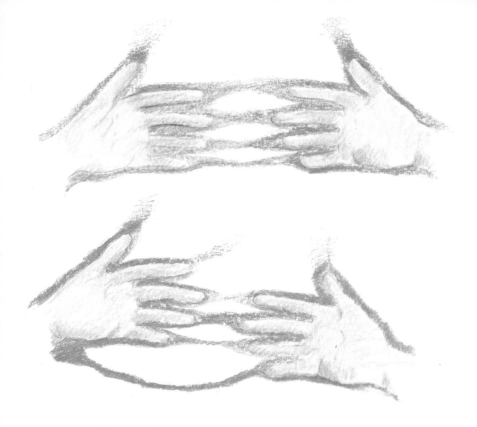

In the top corner, note how the energy field surrounding the fingers on the bottom hand is attracted by its opposite number on the left hand. In the bottom drawing, note how the energy attraction jumps from the right little finger to the left wrist as the right hand is moved downwards. In similar fashion, energy blockages of a patient will 'magnetise' in the hand sensors of the therapist, allowing them to draw away the energy.

A Kirlian photograph showing the energy field surrounding the hands of Tom Griffin. The white lines shooting out represent the energy flow. What is important when assessing such photographs is not the amount of energy but the balance between left and right – that the energies are about equal.

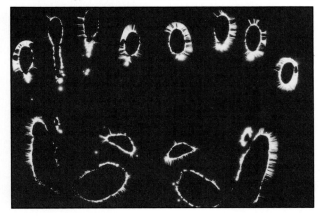

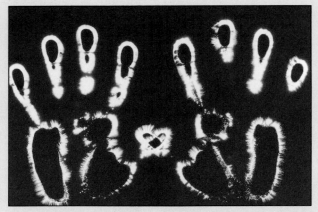

Above: A Kirlian photograph showing the energy field surrounding the hands of Michael O'Doherty. Kirlian photographs will vary according to the time of day they were taken, the emotions, energy levels and mental attitude of the subject at the time, and a host of other factors.

Below: Michael O'Doherty manipulating the energy field surrounding the top of the head of a patient. Energy blockages may show up in the crown energy centre even though the problem that the patient is experiencing may be felt in another part of the body.

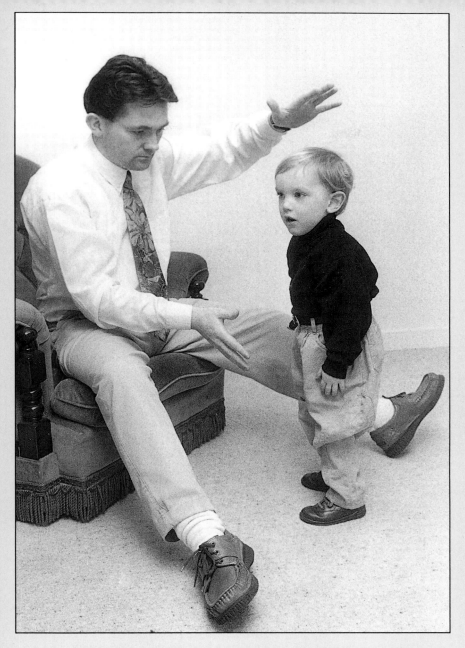

Michael O'Doherty channeling energy in the crown energy centre (at the head) of young Mathew Lowe from Co Leitrim. The energy flowing from Michael's hands will balance the energy field of the young patient. This process is repeated on each day throughout a clinic because, after the first treatment, the energy field will be continually changing until it is balanced.

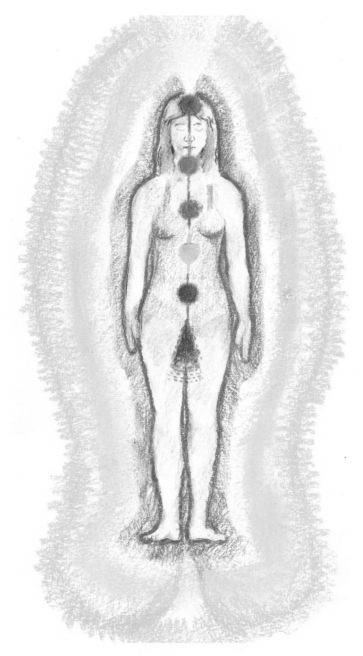

The energy field of a woman after healing has taken place. The energy flows freely through five of the main energy centres, from the top of the head to the base of the spine, and vice versa. The green tinge between the blue layer surrounding the physical body and the outer yellow or golden layer, is quite common. Green represents the healing process in this instance.

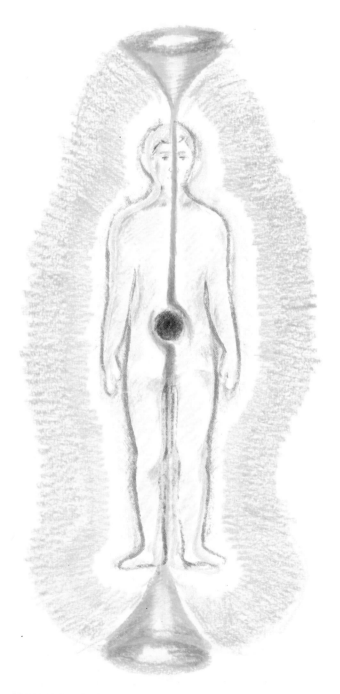

A blocked energy centre in the sacral area. It is blocked at the front and back. The free flow of energy from the top of the head to the base of the spine, and vice versa, is distorted. An illness may show up at a physical, mental or emotional level.

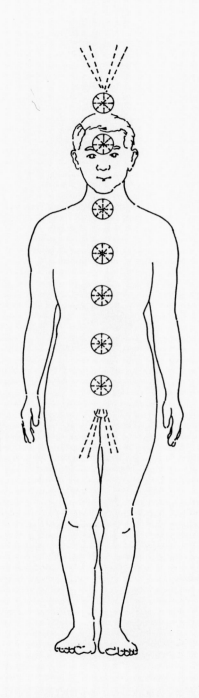

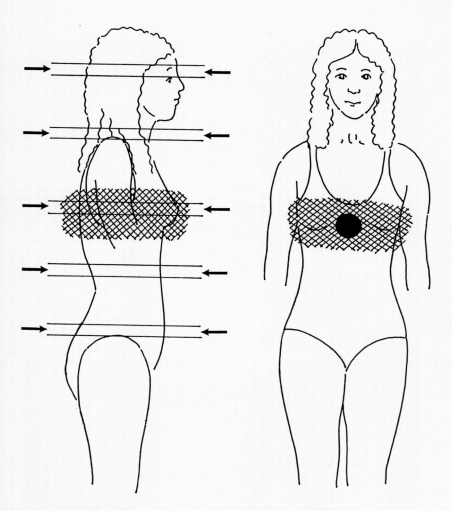

Above: (Left) A side view of a blockage of energy located at the heart energy centre. The free flow of energy that exists in the two energy centres above and below is absent. Energy cannot enter at the front or the back of the energy centre. Eventually, this blockage will lead to ill health if it isn't cleared. (Right) A front view of the blockage in the chest area. The energy has been effectively compacted and can be released through a 'drawing out' motion. The problems associated with an energy blockage with this energy centre can show up in any part of the body, and can affect the mental and emotional states.

Opposite: The seven major energy centres located in the body at the crown, forehead, throat, heart, solar plexus, sacral and base. Universal energy enters at the crown energy centre and flows to the base, while energy enters at the base and flows to the crown. The two energies flux close to the spine and a third type of energy is formed. This is the life energy or vital force that keeps us alive.

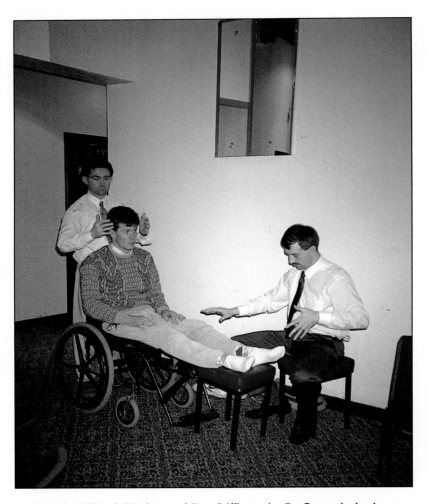

Therapists Michael O'Doherty and Tom Griffin treating Pat Carty, who has been confined to a wheelchair. The aim of the treatment is to rebuild the energy blueprint around the body so that the physical body can then heal itself.

Tom Griffin administering the therapy to Kathleen McCoy. The manner in which the energy field is manipulated sometimes means that patients feel a pulling sensation and have no choice but to walk backwards. This does not necessarily effect the results of the therapy and just shows that the patients energy field can be particularly susceptible to the treatment.

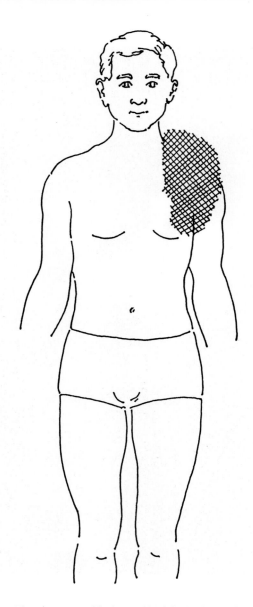

There is an energy blockage on the right shoulder. This may result in pain across the right chest and down the arm. Such a blockage is usually easy to release. This is followed by relief of the pain. This may occur within minutes or up to six months following the treatment.

Michael O'Doherty treating Vivian Convey. The position of Michael's hands indicate that he is 'tuning in' to the energy field. His right hand is sensing the top of the field while his left is probing the front area. This sensitivity in the hands, necessary for the work, is developed over a long period.

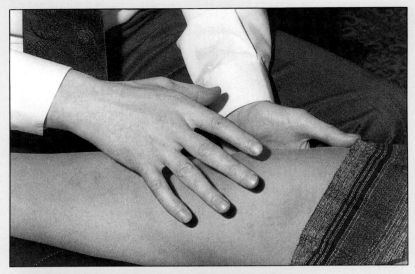

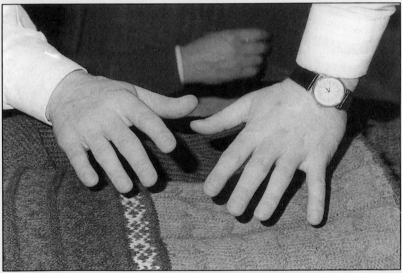

Healing hands. The hands can be used to channel energy into any part of the energy field. In the top picture, the energy is being channeled into the area surrounding the physical problem in the leg. In the lower picture the energy is being channeled into the back.

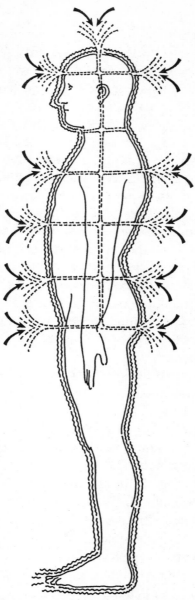

Six of the seven major energy centres running from the top of the head to the base of the spine. With the exception of the crown and base energy centres, the others are all open front to back about four to six inches from the body. The openings are composed of swirling vortexes of energy. Immediately outside the physical body are the start of the various levels in the energy field or aura.

Gradually, over the decades, as scientists have come to recognise that electrical impulses from the body have an effect on health and on the healing process, more investigations into the human energy field have been undertaken. The controversey over Kirlian photography was still raging when, in 1972, Dr Max Toth of the Backster Research Foundation presented for the first time in the West an historic collection of Kirlian photography and phenomena. And at Yale University, Dr Harold S. Burr and Dr F. S. C. Northrup conducted a series of experiments which showed that all living things had an aura or electronic field. They stated that this aura was outside the field of normal human vision and in their experiments they used a machine sensitive enough to measure electrical fields down to one millionth of a volt. They found that when oxygen was removed from the environment of a living organism, its surrounding aura started to contract and continued to do so, without changing its structure, until the organism died, at which point the aura disappeared completely.

In 1979, Dr Robert Becker of the Upstate Medical School in New York actually mapped out the electrical field surrounding the human body. The result looked very much as ancient civilisations had believed it to be. The map was shaped like the body, with a central nervous system. Dr Becker called what he had found the Direct Current Control System and stated that it changed strength and shape with physical and psychological changes in the person. But more significantly, he found particles the size of minute electrons moving through the body's electrical field.

Dr Victor Inyushin, of Kaza University in the USSR, had been carrying out experiments for more than thirty years in this area. Like the Kirlians, he referred to the aura as the bioplasmic energy field and said that it was composed of ions, free protons and free electrons. He concluded that it was outside the recognised realms of physics and chemistry, and that it, in fact, constituted another state of matter, separate from solids, liquids and gases. He also said that this energy was in a constant state of motion and renewal. Even more significantly, he found that there was a balance in the aura between positive and negative forces; when this balance was shifted in favour of one or the other, the organism was affected. A considerable amount of the energy was directed into space, according to Dr Inyushin, and the amount could be measured with sensitive devices.

Other Soviet scientists, working at the Bioinformation Institute of A. S. Popow, conducted a series of intense studies and concluded that living things emit vibrations at a frequency of between 300 and 2000 nanometres. They also found that people capable of transferring energy had a stronger aura than others. The Medical Sciences Academy in Moscow has confirmed this research and, at the time of writing, independent investigations in Britain, the Netherlands, Poland and Germany are supporting this view.

Furthermore, nuclear physicists looking at the human energy field have recently come to the view that it may be composed of ions, electrons and neutral particles.They also believe that the human energy field is a neutral, electrical, strongly ionised substance supporting Inyushin's view that it could be considered as a fourth state of matter.

Science, therefore, traditionally involved in measuring the purely physical realities of life, has now confirmed that various energy fields do exist and that they can be quantified. The Newtonian view of the world, as being composed of only physical matter, no longer holds true. The notion, always held by certain studies in physics, that bodies moving through space had an effect upon each other is now accepted, as is the view that people and their energy fields can also influence each other and that manipulation of these energies can allow people to heal themselves.

THE HUMAN AURA

The aura of the human being is now believed to be a

collection of interconnected electromagnetic waves which penetrate the body and extend beyond it by several feet in roughly an oval shape. The distance from the body depends on the individual, their age, sex and physical/mental condition. People who are more expansive or out-going generally have larger energy fields than average; people who are depressed or ill have a diminished energy field; people who are very ill or about to die have the weakest aura of all.

People who can see the aura talk about a bright rainbow of colours surrounding the body. The brightness of the colours depends on the state of the individual: dark or muddy colours usually indicate a sick person, whether on an emotional, spiritual or physical level. Why only certain people can see this phenomenon is not known, but one theory deals with the structure of the eyes. The normal human eye has some 137 million light receptors, divided into 7 million cones for day and colour vision and 130 million rods for low-light conditions and peripheral vision. It is thought that people who can see auras have a better development of the rods in their eyes.

People can, however, be taught to see the aura using a simple technique. Low-light conditions are best, with a light or dark background. Total relaxation and a positive attitude are necessary. By almost closing the eyes and tilting the head back to a point where you are looking down your nose at the subject, you can succeed, with great patience and practice, in viewing the aura of a person.

In order to diagnose and treat an imbalance of energy in the body, it is not necessary to see the aura physically. It is, however, absolutely essential to be able to feel it and to recognise where the imbalances lie. A properly sensitised hand, in conjunction with a positive attitude and awareness, is able to do this.

The aura is divided into different layers extending outward from the body, each of which can tell something about a particular aspect of the individual. Generally, there are seven layers, with each successive layer being composed of finer substances than the previous. Those closest to the body, the inner layers, are more dense than those further from the body. The layers are also distinguishable by the brightness of their colours and their form. The first, third, fifth and seventh layers contain definite structures, whereas the second, fourth and sixth layers are fluid-like. There are no solid boundaries, however, between the layers: they all intermingle with each other.

Each layer of the aura is related to one of the seven major energy centres or chakras in the body (see Chapter 2). Thus, working up the body from the base of the spine, the first layer of the aura is related to the spinal chakra; the second to the sacrum; the third to the solar plexus; the fourth to the heart; the fifth to the throat; the sixth to the forehead; and the seventh to the head.

The size of a person's aura depends on their energy and make-up. It usually extends to about three feet all around the body. The shape also reveals much about a person's state of health, both physically and mentally. In healthy people, it is an oval shape and extends around the body evenly in all directions. When people are ill, this shape is noticeably distorted, in part or in whole.

In general, the inner layers of the aura relate to physical health. They can change slowly throughout a person's life; as beliefs and health changes, so too do these inner levels reflect the changes and get stronger or weaker. The outer layers of the aura relate to mental stability and they also change as a person's emotions grow and mature. (Human beings are not the only organisms to have energy fields. Animals, too, possess them, although they are far less complex and contain fewer layers.)

The first layer of the human aura is called the physical or 'etheric' body and is directly associated with the physical functions of the body. All sensations, including pain and pleasure, are located here, closest to the physical body, as well as other automatic functions like breathing and heart-beat. This layer is composed of a web of tiny energy lines which are constantly in motion. It extends from about a quarter of an inch to two inches beyond the body. The usual colour associated with this innermost part of the energy field ranges from light blue through to grey. (All of these colours have a significance which will be explained later.)

This layer shows the state of a person's health. If the person is healthy, the layer is even and consistent all around the body; if the person is ill, however, there will be a noticeable bulge along the level where the disorder is located. Thus, this layer is crucial to the diagnosis of a person's condition, since the signs of illness first become evident here, some-times even before the physical symptoms are apparent. If the illness is not treated, the original bulge can push through into the next layers of the energy field, maybe leaving a large gaping hole in the aura eventually. If this happens, it is considered extremely dangerous since other, perhaps more serious diseases can enter the body. If the person's energy field resists this bulging-out process, however (and we can tell this in a clinical session), this indicates that there is an excellent resistance to disease.

The second layer of the aura is called the 'emotional' body and, as its name suggests, is directly associated with the emotional life of the person. Emotional imbalances will manifest themselves here. This layer is fluid and in constant motion, and follows the lines of the physical body, extending about one to four inches beyond it. Its colours are clear and bright in emotionally healthy people, who express pure joy, anger or love, for example; dark and muddy colour indicate a person with problems at this level. In the case of serious illness, this layer of the energy field will have been pushed through from the first level. As with that level, the presence of holes and bulges in the second layer can indicate a disor-der in the body before any physical manifestations have occurred. If left untreated, the continuing deterioration of the energy field may allow other, more serious illnesses to develop over a period of time.

The third layer of the aura, known as the 'mental' body, relates to the individual's mental life. It extends from four to eight inches (sometimes even 12 inches) beyond the physical body and radiates outwards like very narrow fingers, drawing energy from the air into the body. If an illness is present, its energy lines start to droop at that point and less energy is taken in, resulting in that part of the body which most needs energy not receiving it. Yellow is the healthy colour for this third layer. A bright, clear colour indicates a person who is using their mental capabilities to the full. Muddied yellows are associated with problems in the mental field.

This third layer (the mental body) extends into the fourth layer (known as the astral body) at times of high excitement and great energy. Such an interaction between the aura's layers is not unusual. (Part of the second layer also extends into the third layer.) The extent of this interaction depends on how much the emotions dominate the thoughts. If the head rules the heart, then there will be little fusion between the layers; if, however, the opposite is true, then a significant mixing occurs.

The first three layers of the aura (the physical, emotional and mental) are the main ones used in the diagnosis of a problem through bio-energy therapy. All the symptoms of physical disease can be found here, even before the disease itself is apparent. So too with psychiatric disorders: the distortions of the energy field are immediately noticeable. Thus, all the necessary information that we need to treat people is contained in these first three layers.

This is not to say that the other layers of the aura are not involved. The fourth layer, or astral body, is associated with the heart and its energy centre or chakra. The two together – the energy field and the centre – are vitally important and deserve a book on their own. Suffice it to say here that the heart energy centre processes all the higher energies taken in from the head energy centre for use in the lower energy centres. Because the heart is associated with the centre of love, it has a further significance in bio-energy therapy: it is the centre that purifies the energy that is used to heal. Without it there would be no motivation to get better.

The aura's fourth layer is composed of a cloud-like substance made up of much the same colours as the second layer (the emotional body). It extends from about six inches to a foot beyond the body and is a clear sky-blue colour in a healthy individual. It is a vitally important layer since this is where emotional trauma is absorbed and passed on to the other layers and into the energy centres. Much interaction takes place between people on this level, especially between members of the same family, lovers or those that are very close. A negative energy, such as resentment or hate, which has not been absorbed properly can block up this energy centre and cause serious illness if left untreated. When we feel tired, the energy in this layer is depleted and its colour diminished. The astral body also reveals much about an individual's personality and how they relate to others.

It is at this fourth layer of the energy field that people suffering prolonged illness can experience the most blockages. Negative thought patterns or severe trauma can remain here for long periods of time. This is the area that must be treated in bio-energy therapy. The longer this part of the energy field is blocked, the more damage can be done to the health of the individual.

The fifth, sixth and seventh layers of the aura are associated with the higher thought processes. The fifth layer relates to speech and listening. It is called the 'etheric template' body because it contains a copy of everything that is contained in the first, or etheric, layer. It extends from one to two feet beyond the physical body. If there is a problem at the etheric or physical level, it is also necessary to treat the etheric template level in order to balance the energies.

The sixth layer of the aura, the 'celestial' body, is related to love beyond human love, in other words the spiritual side of a person. Composed of gentle pastel shades, this layer seems to radiate out, extending some two to three feet beyond the body. People who have attained a high degree of spiritual maturity and are at peace with themselves and everything around them are very much aware of this part of their energy field. Needless to say, it takes some time to achieve such a state.

The seventh and outer layer of the aura is called the 'ketheric template' body and is associated with the total integration of an individual's physical and spiritual sides. It extends from about two and a half to three and a half feet from the body and contains all the other six layers of the aura within an oval shape. It is composed of tiny threads of gold light and appears to hold the entire energy field together.

COLOURS OF THE AURA

Another factor that can be used in diagnosis is the colours of the aura. These are important to us in our bio-energy therapy, not least because it is easier to related to a colour scheme than to more esoteric notions. Half of the aura may be bright and correctly coloured, while the other half can be murky and discoloured. During a therapy session, we visualise the energy as coming from either the earth or the air, and we channel it through our own heart energy centres to the patient through our hands. This transfer of energy can be used for whatever purpose is necessary – whether it is to release a blockage or replace depleted energy. There are only about a dozen or so basic colours that we use in our work and each has a specific purpose or effect. In addition, the various colours present in a patient's energy field can tell us many things. The colours seem to shimmer and give the impression of being alive.

The colours we use in our therapy sessions have different meanings. The same colour can have positive and negative attributes. Green, for example (of which, incidentally, there are more than forty shades) is the colour of nature and of growth. It is indicative of health and can greatly enhance the healing process when it is used. If the energy field is green overall, it indicates that a healing process is already happening. A clear bright green is a very positive colour; when present, it shows that the person has suffered some kind of trauma but has emerged from it to continue the healing process. A muddy green can indicate envy in a person's make-up. If the green is tinged with yellow (the colour of the mental body), this indicates that the intellect is playing a part in the healing process and that the person is making a conscious effort to get better.

There are over 3000 different colours between all the various shades of green and blue – more than half the registered colours of the spectrum. Like green, blue is also a powerful colour. Dark blues are used for a cooling and soothing effect, particularly if a patient is anxious. Indigo and violet can help greatly with bone healing and stomach and skin disorders. Medical science accepts that ultraviolet can also do the same task. Purple is also a powerful colour, just below violet and indigo.

Blue in a person's aura indicates a strong unconscious intuition, while an overall blue colour to the energy field shows that the person's emotional stability is at its most positive. This is an excellent sign, since an illness often begins at the emotional level, then moves into the energy field and finally manifests itself in the physical body. Light blue in the aura indicates that the person is going through a learning process.

Red is accepted to be the colour of action and activity, and it is generally associated with the lower elements in people. It is also associated with materialistic thinking. When it shows up in the energy field, it is not a good sign and indicates that there are considerable negative aspects to that person. Certain types of red can indicate anger, hate or selfishness. Experiments have shown that when red light is applied to plants, prolonged and unnatural growth results. Tests in the human field have shown that people suffering from heart disorders who have been subjected to bright red colours experience an increase in blood pressure and heartbeat; when greens and blues are substituted, the same people experience a return to normal blood pressure and heartbeat. Pink, also associated with red, when seen in the energy field usually means that the person has a great love within them. This colour can be helpful in calming an over-anxious person.

Orange (a mixture of red and yellow) is another colour associated with energy and action. A clear bright orange, channelled into a patient through bio-energy therapy, has the effect of bringing about wakefulness and activity. Orange is the most frequently encountered colour in people's energy fields and it indicates that the mental and physical states are in constant flux. If someone is recovering from a serious disorder, the presence of orange in their energy field means that they are on the road to recovery. As the healing process continues, green starts to replace the orange. A dirty orange colour in the energy field generally means that the person is repressing something which will eventually manifest itself in the physical body as an illness.

Yellow in the energy field represents the intellect or power of the mind. Various shades have different meanings, ranging from a mustard yellow for cleverness to a bright clear yellow for lofty thoughts.

Gold and silver are at the top of the colour hierarchy when it comes to visualisation. They are both powerful colours to use in healing. Gold can also be used by therapists to protect themselves from released energy entering their own energy fields: by visualising a shield of gold in front of them, they can deflect the unwanted energy. When gold occurs in the aura, it has a bright, blazing colour. Silver is used where it is necessary to send energy to a particular part of the body immediately.

Brown is not often seen in the energy field. It is usually combined with another colour, making it a murky shade. Its presence can indicate that the person is either selfish or materialistic. However, if a rich dark brown shows up in the energy field, it is a positive colour which indicates that a person has a great love for the earth and all things that grow.

Black and white are important as well. Pure black is not a colour at all; it is merely an absence of light. White, on the other hand, is the absolute presence of light. When black shows up in the energy field, it indicates a hole or an absence of light. When white is combined with another colour, it alters that colour for the better, while black alters it for the worse. Grey can also occur in the energy field, but it is a negative colour and usually indicates that a person has a closed mind or a lack of imagination. Grey may also point to a state of depression and it can grow in the aura, most likely leading to a serious illness at a physical and emotional level.

We use all of these colours in our bio-energy therapy sessions to balance the energy field of a patient. In viewing or feeling the energy field, it is possible to detect damage before it manifests itself in the physical body as an illness. But harmonising energy is only the first step on the road to recovery, as mentioned earlier. The rest of the journey involves people taking responsibility for their own lives and health, and regaining their inherent ability to recognise when things are going wrong and correct them before they go too far.

If the colour visualisation that we use in our work seems a strange idea to some people, it is well to remember that various shades of colour and light already affect our lives. Visible light is vital to our well-being and health: a lack of exposure to sunlight, for example, can lead to a deficiency in vitamin D. The fact of the matter is that there are many things about colour and light that we do not fully understand yet, but we cannot ignore them just because we do not understand them.

CHAPTER 4

Harmful Energies

❀

THE EXISTENCE OF ENERGY FIELDS

Some species actually use electromagnetic energy for their survival. Certain species of fish, for example electric eels and rays, use this form of energy as a defence against predators or as an offence to stun prey. Migrating birds, too, use the earth's energies to direct them on their journey. In order for an animal to use these hidden energies, its own energy field must be interacting with the earth's energy field. (So too with us in bio-energy therapy.) Dr Harold Burr of Yale University in a simple experiment demonstrated the existence of an energy field around a live salamander. He started off with the premise that the animal produced an electrical field and that he would be able to interrupt it, thereby creating an electrical current. With the lizard floating in a dish of salt water, he rotated the dish and broke the electrical field. Electrodes placed in the water picked up the current, which was fed into a galvanometer to measure the charge generated; the needle moved from left to right, showing the negative/positive pattern in perfect alternating current. No current was registered when the dish was rotated without the salamander.

Continuing his investigation of energy fields, Burr conducted a series of tests over a 12-month period using student volunteers. Voltage measurements revealed a small daily fluctuation in the subjects' energy fields; females were found to produce a large increase in voltage once a month, in the middle of their menstrual cycles. Further testing with rabbits showed that the monthly increase in voltage was linked directly to ovulation and therefore to changes in the electrical field. Thus, having established that energy fields did exist and that they were connected with biological function, Burr went on to test more than 1000 women at Bellevue Hospital in NewYork. He found abnormal readings between the abdomen and cervix in 102 cases, and 95 of these were later diagnosed as having malignant cancer of the cervix or uteris. In other words, Burr had found changes in the subjects' energy field before the physical symptoms of the disease had shown up. Such measurements of the energy field could obviously prove to be an invaluable early warning system and diagnostic tool for medical science.

The energy field as it related to these experiments could be said to be the sum total of all the small electrical charges that occur as a result of chemical events continually taking place in the body. The significance of the specific data becomes more important when we come to consider how people may have developed various diseases and conditions.

Burr was not the only person carrying out experiments on the energy field. In 1962, Leonard Ravitz was the subject of an article entitled *History, Measurement and Application of Periodic Changes in the Electromagnetic Field in Health and Disease*, published under the auspices of the New York Academy of Science. Ravitz had his energy field continually recorded for several months and found that it reached a maximum positive value around the time of the full moon and a maximum negative value two weeks later. This showed that the energy field was influenced by the changes in the earth's energy field and in the planets.

Thus, the combined results of Burr and Ravitz show that all human beings have energy fields which are influenced by other external energies.

HARMFUL ENERGIES

In our modern world, we are constantly surrounded by sources of energy, natural and man-made, that influence us in many ways that we unaware of because science is only now beginning to investigate their effects. It is easier to understand the concept of the manipulation of human energy that occurs in bio-energy therapy when we know a little about the known effects of other energy sources.

Electricity, microwaves, electromagnetic radiation – all of these energies bombard us in our everyday lives. The scale of their development in recent decades has outpaced our knowledge of their effects on human health, indeed on all living organisms. What all these energies have in common is that they are extremely powerful and undirected; the effects of long-term exposure to them is simply not known, but many recent studies have shown deleterious effects in the short term.

The severe doses of electromagnetic radiation (from high power cables, for example) are becoming more and more threatening to our health, according to dozens of recent reports. It has already been shown to damage the immunity system: in laboratory studies, it was found that 40 percent of the white blood cells (the disease-fighting cells) were damaged when exposed to this radiation and the recovery period was considerable.

There have been some attempts to quantify this threat to human health. For example, the British author Roger Coghill, in his book *Electropollution: How to protect yourself against it*, makes the crucial point that as far as electromagnetic pollution is concerned, our greatest problem is actually knowing when it is taking place since we cannot see or feel it, like we can other sources of pollution such as smog or industrial waste. Despite the known danger to our immune systems posed by this form of energy, there is still little control over the doses of elecromagnetic radiation to which we are exposed. Let us hope that it is only a matter of time before certain standards are applied, in much the same way as exposure to X-rays was limited. When this form of radiation was first introduced, there were effectively no limits on the amount a person could receive, but as knowledge of their effects increased, so the exposure limits to X-rays have been severely curtailed, and will probably be reduced still further in coming years.

Another, more familiar source of energy that has proved harmful is fluorescent lighting. Much research has been done in this area, particularly by the Canadian Centre for Occupational Health and Safety in 1981. Writing in *The Lancet* medical magazine in August 1982, Valerie Beral of the London School of Hygiene and Tropical Medicine found that there was a high incidence of malignant melanoma among workers exposed to fluorescent lighting. This type of lighting emits the same sort of radiation as computer Visual Display Units (VDUs). The glass tube is coated internally with phosphorus and the lighting is activated by an electrode at each end. The phosphorus converts electromagnetic energy into visible light and it also makes organic cells up to a thousand times more sensitive to certain types of radiation. Beral's findings have been confirmed by a number of other reports.The London Hazard Centre, for example, says that there is an increased likelihood of cancer as a result of the energy levels emanating from these lights. It has been acknowledged that the nervous and reproductive systems may be affected by exposure to fluorescent lighting. But by and large, the results of these studies, available since the early 1970s, have not been acted upon to ban or even control such lighting. Its benefits seem to outweigh the potential hazards.

In addition, fluorescent lighting has other potential hazards to do with energy vibrations, which are the subject of ongoing research in many countries. It has been shown, for example, that when lights are flashed at a certain number of cycles per second, this can have an effect on the brain and produce convulsions. Fluorescent lights flash at 100 to 120 times per second and this rate is too high to cause convulsions in humans, but it is not known what other long-term effects such energy vibrations might have.

Visible light is another energy source with well-documented dangers. Professor Ronald Marx of the University of Wales Medical College, a specialist in dermatology, has noted the effects of visible light on the human body. Persistent exposure is one of the most potent causes of skin cancer. Based on research, he also believes that 20 per cent of patients with kidney transplants are affected by skin cancers of one kind or another within ten years of the operation. What is noteworthy here is the fact that Aids patients also have the same tendency to develop a form of skin cancer. There are many theories as to how Aids started: electromagnetic pollution has not yet been ruled out.

Noise is another modern pollutant about which we know little. The British Acoustical Society, for example, has become concerned with the low frequency vibrations, or infrasounds, produced by cars and the effect these can have on drivers. These sounds are at a level of 10 to 20 cycles per second, below the level of conscious human hearing, but they could have a similar effect on health as flickering lights do. The Society has gone on record as warning people that these infrasounds can produce symptoms of recklessness, euphoria, lower efficiency and dizziness due to loss of balance. It is also thought that they could be responsible for the way in which some drivers have been known to drive across busy roadways, apparently oblivious to oncoming traffic.

GEOPATHIC STRESS

A form of natural energy is giving cause for concern in recent years. In particular areas where the earth's magnetic energies have been distorted by such features as underground water, certain mineral concentrations, fault lines and underground cavities, it has been found that the residents' health has been adversely affected. This phenomenon is called geopathic stress. (The uninterrupted or uncontaminated earth's energies, however, are not considered harmful in any way.)

All the experts in this field agree on at least one thing – that bad energies can make people sick. Since we spend approximately one-third of our lives sleeping, the conditions and atmosphere in which we do so are obviously important. Sleep is essential for our well-being. During this time, the body's cells are renewed and repaired – for example, the entire lining of the mouth is washed down into the stomach and digested each day, and we lose some 70,000,000 cells from our intestines every day, all of which need replacing. Sleep is also the body's response to conserving energy.

In geopathically stressed areas, harmful energy waves emanating from the earth are said to interfere with the brain signals we send out in our sleep. These signals are related to the body's restorative functions. If these signals are constantly being interrupted, the theory is that people living in such areas will become ill.

Geopathic stress is not a new or fanciful idea: more than 70 years ago, certain scientists were exploring the idea that where people lived could affect their health in unseen ways. In the 1920s George Lakhovsky, for example, working with the inventor Marconi, proposed the theory that cell problems and dysfunction might be related to radiation influences and that cancers might be caused by sleeping in geographically dangerous locations. He wrote extensively on the effect that a locality's soil and water had on the earth's energies and the effects that this changed energy had, in turn, on human beings. His theory had three basic themes: demographic studies on the distribution of cancers, the geographic studies of soils on which people lived and the types of cancer which appeared to develop most freely, and the consideration of electronics in the particular soils studied.

Lakhovsky conducted a survey in Paris in which he showed that cancers were highest in areas resting on plastic clay and lowest in areas of sand or sandy limestone. Where the soils were complex or mixed, the figures did not show any great difference from the average. He deduced that certain soils deflected cosmic radiation, thereby giving people a double dose of it, leading to harmful effects. He believed that soils which absorbed cosmic radiation were safe. Energy penetration was the crucial factor he found in determining the safety of an area: energy penetration was up to 80 metres in sand and limestone soil, whereas it was just 2 metres in seawater. Hence he concluded that areas with underground water, which refracts radiation, could have an adverse effect on health.

Lakhovsky's work remained largely forgotten until recent years, when Rolf Gordon started to reinvestigate the causes of cancer. (His 26 year old son had died of cancer.) His book, *Are you sleeping in a safe place?*, proposed that cancer, as well as other disorders (such as headaches, arthritis, epilepsy, depression, nose bleeding, TB, meningitis and kidney stones), was caused by harmful earth energies.

Some of Gordon's conclusions may seem fanciful, but we have to remember that he was working with limited resources in an area that was, and still is, underinvestigated. For example, he believed that some traffic accidents were also due to the same earth forces causing a dysfunction in the drivers. Other serious studies in this area include those of Robert Endros and Dr Karl Ernst Lotz, who investigated a number of head-on collisions on a particular stretch of road. The survivors all reported that they had had a complete blackout immediately prior to the accident.

Dr Picard of Moulins, in the French Department of Allier, has also researched the area of geopathic stress and cancer. He studied a group of 42 people whose medical histories were known to him. He looked at their homes and then mapped out all the underground streams in the area. He found that there was a strong correlation between the location of the streams and the houses whose occupants were suffering from cancer. This was particularly evident where two or more streams crossed underground.

Experiments using mice confirm many of these findings.

Animals were placed in the areas thought to concentrate these harmful earth energies and a 20 per cent loss of body weight resulted, accompanied by the development of tumours. A control group of animals, kept well away from the source of the energies, remained healthy.

Research and, more importantly, money for research, into geopathic stress has been lacking, with a few notable exceptions. In 1987, the Research Minister of West Germany, Herr Reisenhuber, allocated money to a research programme (headed by Professor Hildeberthener of the Institute of Pharmaceutical Biology at Munich University) into the harmful effects of earth energies on people.

ELECTRICITY POWER LINES

Another area that has concerned people in recent decades is the potential harmful effects on human health of electricity, particularly from high-powered, low-frequency electricity cable lines. In 1988, the British Central Electricity Generating Board gave half a million pounds towards research into this area. (It should be noted that the electricity industry has a vested interest here because if high-power lines were proved to be harmful, their image of a clean industry would be damaged.) Scientific studies have shown that people who live near such power lines get headaches more frequently than people who do not; they also get depressed more easily and suicide rates are higher in these areas. Eight states in the USA have already banned the siting of new buildings within a certain distance of high power lines as a result of the possible health hazards involved.

Thousands of people could be affected by this potential hazard. In Britain alone, it is estimated that 80,000 people live close to high voltage power lines and high-powered transformers; in the USA, the figure is closer to 250,000. Because we simply do not know the long-term effects of these energies, it may be that it will take a generation or two for any side-effects to show up. Even if corrective action were taken now and the people moved away from the source of the danger, it is possible that the damage caused might take three or even four generations to repair genetically.

Concern over such power lines began in 1974, when Nancy Wertheiner of Denver examined the evidence to ascertain whether there was a link between environmental factors and childhood leukemia. Her results were published in 1979 and Paul Brodeur's book, *The Zapping of America*, and his series of articles in the *New Yorker*, reports on her work. Wertheiner noted that the common factor linking the leukemia cases was that the homes of all the victims were in close proximity to primary and secondary wiring configurations, transforming voltages ranging from 7600 volts to 240 volts for domestic consumption. In many cases, these transformers were attached to poles near people's homes. In conjunction with Ed Leeper, who explained the intricacies of electromagnetism to her, she designed a field-measuring meter and examined the homes of 344 people suffering from cancer. They found that there was an above-average number of people suffering from cancer who lived in situations which gave above-average readings on the meter. As far as they were able to ascertain, the only factor which could give rise to these above-average figures for cancer was the proximity of the people's homes to the transformers.

Closer to home, on the east coast of Ireland, there have been suggestions that the clusters of leukemia associated with the Sellafield nuclear plant in England may not so much be the result of the processing of nuclear waste that goes on there, but perhaps may be caused by the high-voltage power lines that take the electricity so generated out of the region.

Other research on power cables seems to support that done by Wertheiner and others. Russian and British scientists have shown that living organisms react to low-level electromagnetic fields and that cell division can be slowed down, even inhibited, by such fields. Studies have also shown that there is an increase in cancers among those who work in electricity associated occupations. While this is very general in itself, there have been specific studies carried out that make one wary of such power sources. In Stockholm, for example, where all the electrical cables are buried, medical officer Lennart Tomenius investigated 2098 homes with children under 18 years of age. He found that twice as many children who lived near heavy power lines developed cancer, compared to children who lived away from such lines.

The arguments continue to rage between the electricity industry and those who believe that high power sources can, and do, cause ill health. The main type of leukemia that has developed in such locations is lymphatic leukemia.

Among the advocates of the theory that high power lines and transformers can adversely affect human health, it is recommended that there is a minimum safe working and sleeping distance from such power sources. People can do other things also to minimise the risks, for example planting trees between the power lines and their place of work/home, which has the effect of breaking up the emissions. Electrical fields are at their worst at some distance from the pylon, not nearest to it, and they are also more active in the upper floors of a building than lower down. Rooms furthest from the lines should be used for sleeping.

BRAIN WAVES

One of the most important things is to be aware of the potential dangers of these energy sources. The world today is a very different place to what it was a few decades ago. Our towns and cities, even parts of the countryside, are buried in a sea of electromagnetic energy. The world is full of radio stations, radar stations, defence missile systems, mobile receivers, bleepers, car phones, local radio stations and private telecommunications networks. For those who doubt that such a beneficial power source as electricity could be harmful, it is well to remember that many studies show that electricity does have an impact on the human being. Even the simple act of turning on a light switch can have an effect on the brain, by interfering with the its EEG rhythms. Experiments have shown that in the case of identical twins, a change in the EEG of one (by turning on a light switch, for example) affects the other, even when they are in different rooms. This shows that an energy source not only can have an effect on the human mind and body, but also that this effect can be passed on to another through brain waves.

Some people believe that disease can be transmitted through the mind rather than through any known physical pathway. Influenza is a case in point. Many doctors presume that outbreaks of 'flu in schools or other heavily populated buildings are passed on from person to person. In 1977 and 1978, there was an epidemic in British boarding schools in which 100,000 people contracted the virus. The incubation period is three days, but studies showed that the real incidence was random and there was no transmission from person to person. Other studies show that 'flu epidemics can occur in different parts of the world at the same time, and yet neither the wind nor migratory birds would have had the time to carry the virus. Harry Oldfield and Roger Coghill, in their book *The Dark Side of the Brain*, suggest that influenza is caused by brain-to-brain transmissions, when the brain's normal healthy signals are interfered with and the end result is 'flu.

ELECTROMAGNETIC SOURCES

Part of the modern problem of harmful energy sources is that there is still no comprehensive system to tell people when they are in potentially dangerous areas. However, some research has been done recently by Stephen Perry, a Birmingham doctor, who has designed a system to register the initial symptoms of electricity orientated stress. His study of 600 suicides in the Birmingham area showed that at homes where the magnetic field was relatively high, the risk of depressive illness was one and a half times greater than in areas where the magnetic field was about average. Such a field can be caused by electrical wiring, power lines and transformers. Researchers in Italy and in the USSR have shown that overexposure to electromagnetic fields are associated with high blood pressure.

In 1964, US researchers at the Johns Hopkins School of Medicine found that children born with Down's Syndrome correlated with mothers who had been given excessive X-rays and with fathers who had been working near the microwave transmitters of radar stations. The men were found to have a higher than normal proportion of chromosome defects in their blood. Seven years later, in one 16-month period at Fort Rucken Air Base in Alabama, army helicopter pilots who had been exposed to radar were found to have fathered children with birth defects: seventeen children were born with clubfoot, where four is the average.

In 1976, a sophisticated radar system was installed on the Cape Cod peninsula with a 1200 foot pyramid of reinforced concrete. It was a PAVE-PAWS system, with 10,000 solid-state radiating elements within it, each of which was individually computer-controlled to form a single beam. In May 1979, the Air Force admitted that because of the known sensitivity of the central nervous system to electromagnetic fields, the possibility could not be ruled out that exposure to PAVE-PAWS radiation might have some effects on people's health. In other words, they did not know the short-term effects, never mind the possible long-term ones.

Crucial to these long-term effects is the half-life of natural materials. This is the amount of time taken for half of their energy to dissipate. Half-lives vary for different substances, ranging from a matter of moments to decades. One of the main problems with energy waves is that they are cumulative and tend to build up in the system. Physicist Professor Herbert Frohlich of Liverpool University has studied the biological effects of microwaves and concluded that long-term interaction between microwaves and human beings will interfere with brain transmissions.

Computers, both in the home and in the office, are the biggest boom area in the last ten years. They offer enormous benefits, but they may also carry great risks, maybe the greatest health risk of the years to come. VDUs are adding greatly to our annual intake of radiation: operators might expect to get one-third of their annual dose of radiation from their machines. In the USA alone, there were more than 30 million VDUs in operation at the time of writing, while Britain had about eight million. Many people might think there is little difference between a VDU and a television screen. But there is a great difference. Firstly, people watch television from a distance – not so with a VDU, which is constantly bombarding the user with cathode rays emanating from its screen. A VDU operates by firing electrodes at a phosphorus-coated screen and deflecting them onwards by means of magnets to form the required image. Because they are so cost-effective, we are likely to see more VDUs in public places such as supermarket check-out points, cash dispensers, production processes, bars and so on.

VDUs emit radiation in the ultraviolet (UV) and non-ionising frequencies. Skin cancers have been known for decades to come from UV radiation, but the effects of such radiation concentrated for long periods on the upper portion of the body, including the head, are only just being realised. A study by Mays Swicord of the United States Food and Drug Administration in the early eighties found that the DNA helix (each person's genetic blueprint) is in danger of fracturing and possible mutation as a result of such exposure. Other studies have found that eyesight may be damaged as a result of exposure to VDUs. There is also a correlation between extremely low levels of radiation and ill health. Changes in the pattern of brain waves are also associated with VDUs; this manifests itself as behaviour problems, such as sluggishness, depression and an inability to concentrate, which may eventually turn into ME and chronic disability. Dr Arthur Guy, an adviser to IBM, has found that the energy fields in front of some screens, even at low intensities, induce a significant electrical current in human tissue.

The long-terms effects of such radiation on VDU operators is not known. Prolonged use may increase the chances of miscarriages and birth defects. The General Council of Trade Unions in Japan surveyed 13,000 VDU workers, of whom 4500 were women; 250 of these women had become pregnant while working with VDUs and 91 had had abnormal pregnancies, with eight miscarriages, eight premature births and five still births.There was a direct relationship between the amount of time the women spent working at the VDU and their pregnancy-related problems. At the time of writing, there is no overwhelming body of evidence to prove that pregnant women operating VDUs are endangering themselves and their unborn children.

We do not know the effect of long-term, low-dosage irradiation, but one example may give us a clue for the future. In 1948, Israel started an irradiation programme to eradicate ringworm from the heads of 20,000 children. Some 26 years later, Elaine Ron and Barouch Modan followed up the cases and found that, compared to the normal population, 3 times the expected average had died from tumours of the head and neck, and that 2.3 times the expected average had died from leukemias. A more recent study, undertaken in 1988 by Barouch Modan, concluded that the relevance of this data went way beyond the nuclear industry and that it touched the full spectrum of energy resources. He also said that it was becoming increasingly difficult to isolate the benefits of electromagnetic energy from the potential risks and that electromagnetic energy must be considered an environmental hazard until it was proven otherwise. If we are to accept this, there are huge implications for the way we live today, not least because we have allowed the build-up of so many different forms of energy without any thought to the harmful effects or how to deal with them.

There have been very few studies which take a global view of this build-up of sources of energy. One that is worth quoting is the 1979 nationwide survey of population exposure to UHF and VHF radiation, undertaken by Richard Tell and Ed Mintapay of the USA's Environmental Protection Agency. Five hundred locations around 15 major cities were covered, amounting to 20 per cent of the population. They found that one per cent of the people surveyed were exposed to the maximum limit permitted in the USSR; the maximum permitted limit in the United States was much higher. Perhaps the most frightening thing about these statistics was that the vast majority of people exposed to these levels of radiation were totally unaware of it.

Examples of radio-transmitting frequencies correlating with health irregularities are fairly numerous. Again, we look to the USA for research in this area. In McFarland, California, 13 children have developed cancer since 1975, an above-average figure. The town has a population of just 6000 people, and it has been suggested that the cause of the cancers may lie just up the road – in Delano, where 'The Voice of America' radio station broadcasts to Latin America and Asia, using 250,000-watt transmitters. The radio signals are beamed directly over the citizens of McFarland.

Another such case documents that at Lualualei in Hawaii between 1979 and 1985, an abnormally high rate of cancer (4 times the average) was prevalent among the children of the town. Located nearby is the US Navy Communications Centre and it has been suggested that there is a connection between it and the cancers. Moving across the ocean to Gibraltar, where the British have a huge communications centre, the incidence of cancer is so high that a special recuperation unit has been set up in Britain to help people who have contracted cancer. The numbers are said to be running currently at 150 people a year.

To understand the significance of all this, it is worth going back to the 1960s, when research conducted by Madeleine

Dornothy showed that the immunity system of rats exposed to a magnetic field in an experimental situation was effectively reduced by 40 per cent. If the same rats were removed from the magnetic field, it took them about three months to return to normal. But long-term exposure to such a field would undoubtedly have serious side-effects.

SICK BUILDINGS

Another aspect of pollution has come to light in recent years with the emergence of what are known as sick buildings. It is, of course, the people who work in these buildings who are sick, more often than would be expected when compared with the population as a whole. Complaints such as tension, depression, headaches and lack of energy are common.

There are a number of factors which should be taken into account when locating a building. Firstly, geopathic stress zones should be avoided. (It is possible to know if one lives in such an area quite simply: the volume or reception of the television does not work properly and there is undue inexplicable interference.The radiation emanating from that break in the earth is in the VHF range and this could be what causes the interference.) Secondly, people should be protected against electromagnetic fields. And thirdly, non-toxic and natural building materials should be used in the construction.

Ions, or electrons freed from their atoms, also influence people's health. Negative ions are good for human health, whereas positive ions are not so good. Natural porous materials, such as brick and stone, will allow negative ions to pass through them, but plastic, glass and concrete do not. Machines in offices are constantly discharging positive ions and thus it is reasonable to say one could be at risk working in an modern office. Again, there are studies to support this theory. In 1981, Leslie Hawkins of Surrey University's Department of Occupational Health found that when a negative ion generator was installed in offices, unbeknown to the people working there, the incidence of headaches, nausea and drowsiness fell by 50 per cent.

It is not just machines or the location that determine whether a building is sick or not. In 1987, Dr Stephen Perry of Birmingham and Laurence Pearl, a statistician from Wolverhampton Polytechnic, spent six months surveying 49 high-rise apartment blocks, built several years previously. There were 6000 people living in 3000 housing units. They divided their sample group into two: those living near the rising cables which supplied the blocks with their power and those living farther away from them. The first group had a much higher incidence of depression (22 out of 31) than the second group; if there were underfloor storage or heating systems (emitting even more electromagnetic waves) the figure rose to as high as 82 per cent. This study supported earlier studies showing that people living near high-voltage cables had an increased level of suicides.

RADIATION

Again and again, it comes across that we do not really know what the side-effects of such energy sources are or what the long-term effects may be. In relation to radiation, it is worth taking a look at the changing exposure limits to X-rays over the years. In 1900, the exposure limit was 10 Rems per day, which meant that there was effectively no limit. By the mid-1930s the limit had dropped to 36 Rems per year; by 1957 it was 5 Rems per year and in 1989 the limits were again under review.

The truth of the matter is that we did not know what the safe limits were until the side-effects started to manifest themselves. Long-term studies are beginning to show that radiation effects may not become apparent for decades or even generations. What we can say for sure is that the sources of radiation have increased dramatically in this century and we have not yet learned their effects. We take in radiation from numerous sources, many of them natural. The glossy PR booklet supplied to visitors at Sellafield Nuclear Power Station gives an interesting breakdown: they claim that internal radiation (from eating and drinking) accounts for 17 per cent of our intake; terrestrial rays account for 19 per cent; cosmic rays for 14 per cent; radon and thoron for 37 per cent; and medical (mainly X-rays) for 11.5 per cent. The rest, they say, including nuclear radiation, is a mere 1.5 per cent.

BENEFICIAL ENERGIES

The bottom line in all of this is that we are surrounded by energy sources which are constantly interacting with our own energy field and changing it. Bio-energy therapy is concerned with using these energies to make people better. The energies used in the therapy and those other potentially harmful energies should not be confused, nor should it be imagined that because other energies can be harmful, that bio-energy therapy is also potentially harmful. The central function of the therapy is to ensure that the brain is sending out the correct signals to those cells of the body that are not functioning. The idea of mental and emotional disharmony having a major role to play in disease, and the concept of this being correctable by energy balance, are both concepts which will be familiar to the reader at this stage. These concepts are fundamental to bio-energy therapy.

CHAPTER 5

Working in the Clinic

❀

It is an irony that nobody wants to be sick and yet the world is full of sick people. Perfectly healthy people fall ill during their lives for no reason that they can make out and then the disease can disappear as suddenly as it started. This is traumatic and often inexplicable, at least in conventional medical terms. But it can be explained in energy terms.

When people are born, they have an innate ability to heal themselves naturally. But somewhere along the line, for a variety of reasons, the body loses that ability and falls ill. Some people will get well eventually, but others will not. It is not only their physical body that is sick; there are also other invisible, equally important aspects that are affected. A disorder that shows up on the physical level will also affect the energy centres and the energy field or aura, and therefore shows up as energy imbalances and depletions. It is vital that these are corrected if the physical body is to get well again.

The basis of bio-energy therapy is the balancing of both the energy centres and the energy field. This, in turn, activates the body's own ability to heal itself. As therapists, we use the extra-sensory ability we have developed to do this, in combination with the energies that are all around us. When the energies of a patient are balanced, it is generally only a matter of time before the physical manifestation of the disease clears up.

In some cases, however, even when the energies of a patient appear to us to be balanced, there is still no change in the physical condition. We simply do not know why this happens. It could be that some people are just not ready for the therapy, so even though their energies are balanced some other factor, perhaps within themselves, will not allow them to take that final step which would result in an improvement of their condition. In other cases, we can explain the problem. Many people who attend our clinics are on medication. After about four or five days of treatment, they feel much better but they continue on their medication as before. Often, what we end up treating is the side-effects of the prescribed drugs, which can be worse than the original complaint. The minimum we would require in cases like this is a review of the medication following the bio-energy therapy. But in many cases, this just does not happen. Usually, the medication is only dealing with the symptoms of the disease, not the causes. While we can help such people in our clinics, the treatment can be nothing more than a short-term holding exercise. It obviously makes our job very difficult if patients continue to soak themselves in a drug culture which has effectively failed them.

BIO-ENERGY CLINICS

We treat a wide range of diseases and conditions in our clinics, ranging from the emotional to the mental to the spiritual and, naturally enough, the physical. The common feature with most of our patients is that their lives have been dramatically affected by illness with their dignity and ability to lead a full and active life suffering as a result. No one is as vulnerable as the person who is sick and unable to help themselves. The medical profession can tell them that all that can be done has been done and usually a range of drugs is prescribed to numb the pain, both physical and emotional. (Many doctors today, however, realise that they do not have a monopoly on people's health and that alternative routes do exist. Such open-minded doctors refer their patients to other therapists.) The patient and the family are on their own, without hope. If the sick person has a long life expectancy, say of thirty or forty years, then the pressure and strain on those who have to cope with the situation can be unbearable. Hope, the single most important constituent of being alive, has been taken away from such people. It must be allowed to grow and develop again.

People who are very sick will go to great lengths to find a cure for their ailment. Apart altogether from general practitioners, specialists, consultants and hospitals, many of our patients have done the 'alternative medicine' rounds already before they discover bio-energy therapy: they may have tried faith-healers and a host of others, spending a great deal of time, energy and money in their efforts. When they get to us, we tell them that the key to their own health lies inside themselves, that it has been there all along and that they have the ability to heal themselves if only they would realise it. But in order for this to happen, their own ability has to be activated by the therapy. This may sound facile, even ridiculous, to many people suffering from a prolonged illness, but the fact of the matter is, it works for many.

The depersonalisation of healthcare in our modern world is an important issue. People need to take responsibility for their own welfare. Good health cannot be bought, unlike many other commodities, except perhaps in the area of organ transplants. But, by and large, wealth is no respecter of health. Everyone has the right to good health, regardless of age of income.

For many of those who come to our clinics, it is their last chance to get well. Without wishing to sound too off-putting or negative, our clinics are in many instances a last resort. The bottom line for many of our patients – not all, we stress – is that if they fail to benefit from the therapy, then there is no place else they can go, because they have been there already. Most people who attend the clinics really want to get help; even after decades of pain, they still have a spark of hope left and it is our job to rekindle that spark and lift their depression. Others who come have no expectations at all and their initial reaction to the way in which the therapy is administered is one of great curiosity. Sometimes, but not very often, a person is openly hostile to the therapy and then it can be extremely difficult to get a positive result.

The attitude of mind of patients is important, even crucial, to the therapy: the expectation that they *can* get well has at least got to cross their minds – not the moment they walk into the clinic, but at some stage during the treatment, it has to be a part of it. This thought will give them a belief in themselves, engendering a goodwill which can go a long way towards a successful outcome.

At this stage, it is worth digressing for a moment to examine the conscious decision people take to come to a bio-energy clinic. By the very act of deciding to attend, some people have already activated the desire to get well within themselves, even though they might not be conscious of it. This, in turn, will activate the healing process at either a conscious or an unconscious level, so that the life energy may already have started to work before the treatment is even administered. After some four or five days' treatment, the energy centres and the energy field should be balanced or at least in the process of balancing themselves. In some cases, further work may be required on the patient's energy field in the future. Patients may not get immediate physical relief from their pain – it can take hours, days, weeks or even months for the physical body to experience a change for the better. There is no hard and fast rule as to how long this healing process will take at the energy level or how long before it affects the physical body. It is also impossible to say who will and who will not benefit from the therapy, but what can be said with a fair degree of certainty is that, once the energies have been balanced in a patient's energy field, the conditions exist to allow them to heal their own illness.

A TYPICAL SESSION

Each bio-energy clinic starts with a talk on the nature of the therapy and the underlying principles involved. We try to get people to rethink their conditioning about illness and the alleged infallibility of the medical profession. It is certainly not our intention to discredit the profession, but this seed of doubt has to be sown to break the imprint made on people's minds that they cannot get better. If they continue to believe firmly in the inevitability of their suffering, then there is little point in going on with the clinic. In addition, we explain to patients about the whole depersonalisation of their health, how this has taken place and how it is affecting them every day of their lives. We tell them that the key to good health lies within themselves and that they have to view their health as part of themselves, not as something alien and apart from them.

The talks are not predetermined; each day they may revolve around a different theme. The main point is to get people to start thinking for themselves, to break down the barriers of prejudice and conditioning in order to get them to wrest responsibility for their own health from those to whom they have handed over the control. Above all, patients must believe that what they are doing in this regard is right. That is not to say that they must believe everything we say, with no doubts, but rather that they must believe that they are doing nothing wrong in changing their views. If this is not believed, they may end up with feelings of guilt which are just as harmful as many other negative emotions.

THE TREATMENT

Some 300 or 400 patients may attend one of our bio-energy clinics. Patients are generally treated standing up. This is not necessary (indeed many patients come to the clinics in wheelchairs), but it is the best position from which to manipulate the energy field. It also facilitates the flow of both cosmic and earth energy. As the treatment proceeds, we try to demystify the subject by telling the patient about the various flows of energies within and outside their bodies and about the energy centres. We also alert them to the fact that they may feel a tingling or a heat with the treatment and not to be alarmed at this.

As previously mentioned, the energy centres (the 7 major ones and 21 minor ones) are vital for survival. If they are blocked or depleted, ill health will result. It cannot be stated with complete certainty that a blocked or depleted energy centre causes all disease and illness, but it is possible to say that an imbalance, which is how we describe these conditions, will mean a slowing down of the recovery rate on a physical level. If the energies are balanced, on the other hand, the body will heal at a much faster rate. What our patients come to accept is the fact that they are composed of more than just flesh and bones: they are also composed of energy and this energy can affect their lives.

In addition to these energies, people come to accept that there are many things which they cannot see but which do nevertheless have an affect on their health and well-being. A person's will, which cannot be physically touched, is important here and has a bearing on how they respond to the treatment. The will is diminished when we are sick and it can sometimes collapse altogether, leading to a complete inability to help ourselves. So on that level, the therapy is about restoring the will to fight and be well again. People only realise that their will has been diminished when they begin to get it back again and this realisation can be a great boost to the therapy.

There are other important aspects involved in the therapy. For example, people begin to realise the importance of harmony within themselves and with their friends, family and surroundings. Time and again, patients have said to us that their lives have changed and it is all due to us; in response, we say that it is actually due to themselves, that we have simply reawakened something that was within them all the time, but that they had forgotten. Patients rediscovering their own harmony is one of the most gratifying aspects of our work.

The barriers that people may have had on entering the

clinic usually come down at this point and their preoccupation with a drug-based healthcare system is overcome. Having tapped into the life force, they suddenly realise that they do not have to look upon suffering as their normal lot and accept blindly what institutions hand down to them. They finally realise that the only limits they have are the ones they set themselves.

All of these concepts might be difficult for people who have never attended a clinic to understand, but we have witnessed these major changes in people again and again. The testimonials that people have given us of their own free will bear this out. People's lives *are* changed and most are never the same again. By the time they leave the clinic, they have arrived at a different view of life: they know about the life energy and that they are surrounded by an energy field which affects their health.

What actually happens in bio-energy therapy is hard to explain. We have to tap into the energy field of the patient, which is at its most dense closest to the physical body. Using the ability that we have developed, we can sense where there are blockages and depletions in both the energy field and in the energy centres. A balancing of the energy field will automatically transfer itself to the energy centres and vice versa. The imbalances are rectified by either drawing off energy to release a blockage or putting in energy to replenish a depletion. The energy field of the patient and our own energy fields interact, and our energy fields act as a conduit for the life force. This interaction, combined with our hand movements which manipulate the patient's energy field, will bring about the desired result. It is important to realise that we are not the source of this energy. While it is possible to treat people using our own energy, this method is debilitating. We have noticed in cases where patients are very ill, with terminal cancer for example, that those patients will unconsciously draw on us when we are working with them. We have to be alert to this because we could become drained very quickly and there are ways we can guard against it to ensure that we can continue working throughout a clinic.

Many patients are surprised when we are able to diagnose their problem without being told or without having physically touched them. We have come across numerous examples where people have come to be treated for back pain, for example, and we have discovered something else wrong which they did not tell us about. (Some patients are embarrassed by a particular illness they have and so they do not mention it.) But their surprise shows that they have missed the point about the therapy and the way in which it works. It is simply not necessary for us to know how our patients have been diagnosed by medical science in order to treat them successfully. Once we have tapped into the energy field of the patient, we can tell what is wrong on an energy level and treat the problem. Very often the area of the energy field that we treat bears no relationship to the corresponding physical area. For example, if a patient has a problem in their neck, we do not necessarily treat the energy field around the neck; we could work on a part of the energy field far away from where the pain is centred.

Our hands become the sensors, mediators and transmitters of energy. They can receive and send out signals at an energy level. Where that energy ends up depends on how we focus our will, since we can direct energy mentally to where it is most needed using our conscious will and that part of our heart that desires to help a sick person who cannot help themselves.

The use of the will to direct energy developed in us at the same time as the sensory ability to detect the imbalances. We have to be very aware of how we have developed these abilities if we are to continue to treat people successfully. We must always be willing to help people who are less fortunate than ourselves and we have to have a compassion for our patients. The mental ability can be used alone, but without the compassion it is a lesser force. Being full of compassion without any mental brake or direction would not be the ideal situation either; what would happen quite simply is that we would be exhausted after treating a few people and be unable to continue. The balance of will and compassion is thus important in our work.

To our sensory abilities, the atmosphere within each clinic at an energy level is always different, just as two working days are never alike. However, some features are predictable, such as the fact that patients on the first day are expectant, on the second day they are getting used to the way the therapy is administered, on the third day they may feel a lot worse than when they started, and on the fourth day they are on a high and feeling much better. The fact that there are hundreds of people, sometimes as many as 400, in the one room means that there is a tremendous amount of energy build-up and that energy can be tapped into while patients are being treated.

Sometimes in a clinic there are a few people with a particularly negative attitude towards the therapy. There is nothing about the way they are dressed or their physical appearance or expression that tells us this; we simply sense it immediately on an energy level. Such patients can affect the potential results on others in the immediate vicinity, so their negative energies have to be neutralised as quickly as possible for everyone's sake. Usually such patients have been extremely ill for a long time and they cannot be blamed for what they feel. Turning their energies around during a single clinic usually requires a lot of work, but it is vital if they are not to have a disruptive effect on the other patients.

One of the crucial factors in helping to reverse such negativity is the harmony between the therapists who work in our clinics. The simple reason for this is that a number of people working in harmony will achieve greater results than the sum total of their individual efforts. We make a link with one another and are sensitive to each other's moods, so that the total capacity of the clinic is increased and everyone has a good attitude towards their work. If there is disharmony between us, this will cause an obstruction in the clinic which, in itself, will not stop the healing process as far as the patients are concerned, but it will make our job more difficult and consequently slow down the healing process. One of the ways we achieve this harmony is by doing some exercises together each day for several minutes before the clinic begins, to help clear our minds for the coming work.

The therapists we employ join us on a six months' probationary period. The desire to help people is the most important motive. Learning how to diagnose what is wrong with a human energy field and how to treat a person using bio-energy takes a lot of time and patience. Progress is monitored at all stages and the therapists are introduced to the various aspects of the work gradually, so there is a continual development and learning process. The desire to help people has to transcend the uniqueness of the therapy and the way in which it is administered. For the therapist, it involves a change in mental attitude, a change in the way illness and life are viewed. Patients who come to us with the most horrendous diseases deserve the most we can give then, regardless of age, sex, race or religion. Taking a patient onto the floor to be treated is a declaration of intent to help that person and to do the very best that can be done to restore their ability to heal themselves. We have to be able to see beyond the physical nature of the disease to the potential of the person in front of us.

The way in which we treat people once they are on the floor is simple enough to describe. We move our hands down in front of a patient's body in a criss-crossing motion in front of the seven major energy centres; starting at the crown energy centre at the top of the head, we work down through the throat centre, the heart centre and so on, until we get to the centre located at the base of the spine. Then we do the same at the back of the body. While we are doing this, our intention to help the patient is very important and we can say in all certainty that as long as the good intention is there, then no harm can come to the patient through the therapy.

These movements have two effects. Firstly, we tap into the energy field of the patient and, secondly, we can start to balance the energy between the seven energy centres. Some patients at this point will start to move backwards or forwards along the floor and this means that we have successfully tapped into their energy field. This involuntary movement can sometimes indicate, in a general way, how receptive the patient is to the therapy. More specifically, it gives an indication of where the imbalance in their energy field lies. When we pass our hands over a patient, we feel a number of things through the palms of our hands – heat, tingling, cold, pressure. These sensations are clear indications to us of where the problem lies at an energy level. In many cases, we pick up a disorder at this energy level long before it manifests itself in the physical body.

Some patients can be frightened and need reassurance when they experience an unseen force moving them involuntarily along the floor, without us putting a hand near them. Apart altogether from the diagnostic value to us, these movements help others who are watching in so far as their scepticism is rapidly dispersed when they witness something like this. When it comes to their own turn, this scepticism can be broken down completely when they feel a cold, hot or tingling sensation as we work on them. Patients soon come to believe that we are working on the non-physical level of their being. Once they accept that, in combination with the hope they have of being helped, there is very little to stop them helping themselves. Their expectations and hopes are raised at this point and they begin to look at the therapy and at us differently. They are actively discouraged from looking on us as 'gods' – we constantly remind them that the power lies within themselves. This aspect of what we do cannot be stated often enough.

Throughout a clinic, patients come to look upon us as

being a positive force between themselves and their illness; their attitudes will change gradually for the better and this is the point at which they will begin to view their whole existence in a different light. The beliefs they had when they first entered the clinic no longer hold true: they have seen and experienced phenomena which, in general, they cannot explain. They usually feel better, both physically and mentally, but the fundamental thing that has changed is their view of illness and what it is.

Most patients know only the pain and suffering of disease and the effect it has on their lives. They do not know what has been the cause of their illness. Often it is necessary to go back in order to go forward: for example, the death of a close relative or friend in the past may have traumatised a person, causing a distortion of their energy field which has eventually led to a physical illness. In other cases, we have noted energy blockages far away from the site treated by the patient's doctor. Talking to the patient during bio-energy treatment, we may find that they have suffered a blow or fall or other trauma in an area corresponding to the energy field, perhaps in their childhood. Usually the injury does not show up in the corresponding area of the body, but we have treated scores of cases where we have balanced the energies and the physical disorder for which they were being treated then disappeared.

Other patients we have treated have been told by doctors that their illness was imaginary, 'all in the head', and that there was nothing wrong with them. In many of these cases, there is a problem at an energy level but the physical symptoms complained of do not match any named disorder or condition. The pain is no less real for all that and this has shown up in the energy field.

No two patients or their energy fields are the same and each has to be treated on an individual basis. Although every aura is roughly the same oval shape, sizes differ. Because of this, we have to work at a distance, sometimes up to fifteen feet, from a patient to get a correct reading on exactly where the problem lies. Once it is located, the treatment proper can begin.

When an energy imbalance is present, it shows up in the energy centres themselves, which may be open or closed at the front or back, and in the energy field or aura. It is an intuitive decision how we treat the imbalance: we can either treat it directly at source or we can treat it through a different part of the energy field, which usually takes longer. A blockage or a depletion of energy is treated using two basic movements. The first involves a drawing-off of energy and the second an accumulation motion. With the palms facing the patient, energy is drawn off by moving the hand in an anticlockwise direction at a distance of about eight inches from the body. Sometimes we will draw our hands much further away from the body and shake them from time to time in order to release energy that has 'clung' to them. This feels a little like static electricity to us. Conversely, the process of putting energy into an energy field involves moving the hand in a clockwise direction towards the affected energy centre. We may ask a patient to sit down in order to put energy straight into the solar plexus centre which acts as a revitalisation centre for all the others.

One of the facets of the therapy that people find curious is the fact that it is not necessary for us to know where the energy blockage or depletion is in order to help people to rebalance their energies. All that is really necessary for us to know is that certain movements will have certain effects and on that basis it is possible to help people. However, we are able to tell patients where they are feeling pain or discomfort physically, as well as sensing non-physical mental, emotional and spiritual problems.

The therapy becomes highly personal at this point. A trust develops between us and the patient who is then able to accept more easily what we are doing and how we are doing it. As we walk around them, apparently waving our hands senselessly in the air, the patient no longer feels foolish, standing, as they are, in stocking feet surrounded by hundreds of other people. Once the patient feels the therapy beginning to work, then a deep relationship forms, which grows as the treatment continues over the four or five days of the clinic. Each day, we check their energy field, since it rebalances itself after each treatment; it can be stronger or weaker, or breaks may have developed or sealed. The first and last movements in the treatment involve criss-crossing the hands at the front and back of the patient's energy field, which has a naturally balancing effect on the energy centres themselves.

Many patients express alarm when they find that at some point during a clinic they actually feel worse than before they came to us. This normally happens on the third day of a clinic. This apparent worsening of the condition is actually good in itself and shows that the treatment is working. We call this stage the 'healing pain', because the disorder has been brought to the surface and the energies are balancing out as part of the cleansing process. For many patients, this is the last time they will experience the symptoms of their condition before they are totally cured. This restoration of the body's natural ability to heal itself, activated by the rebalancing of the life energy, can occur by the third day for some patients – it varies from person to person.

Patients do come to believe, regardless of what changes have or have not come about, that the therapy is something to be taken seriously. It is also important for people who at the end of a clinic have had no change in their condition at least to retain the hope that they might benefit at a later stage, either through attending another clinic or by accepting the fact that the therapy may take longer to work for them. There are numerous cases where people have found relief from their disorder four or even five months after the treatment. The single most important piece of information that people gain from a clinic is a hope and belief in their natural ability to heal themselves. And this belief continues to work long after the treatment is finished.

This hope is important no matter how bad a person's condition appears to be. We know from experience that even the most serious diseases and conditions have regressed and disappeared following therapy. There is therefore hope for everybody. This is such an important point that it would be irresponsible of us not to examine it in detail. Many of our patients who have suffered prolonged illness come to us with a profound sense of hopelessness. Sometimes this hopelessness has been ingrained in them by either the medical profession, which in some cases has sent people home to die, or by the church, whose teachings instill in people a sense that suffering is necessary for salvation. Both institutions are less than helpful in giving people hope to rid themselves of pain and suffering. Of course, this is not to say that individuals within these institutions are not enlightened and take a different view – we are generalising here. Combined with this negative mental state of mind, the close family and friends of the sick person can sometimes maintain a 'death watch' over them, adding to the sense of hopelessness already there. Attending a clinic and having hope renewed is therefore vitally important for such people.

While it is good for people to feel hopeful about their recovery with the therapy, a balance has to be struck between this and raising their expectations too high, to the point where they cannot be fulfilled. It is not possible for us to say who will or will not benefit, but from experience we can say with a fair degree of certainty on the second or third day, when we have noted people's reactions and the way they are progressing, who will be cured on a long-term basis. What this means is that if, on the last day of a clinic, certain patients have no pain and the disorder has been a relatively minor one, then we have a high expectation that the disorder will not recur.

In general, we have a 70 per cent success rate with the

therapy. This is not to say that 70 per cent of patients are totally cured and their lives turned around as a result of coming to us. What we mean is that there has been some sort of change in 70 per cent of the people that attend us. We have successfully treated a variety of diseases and conditions, including asthma, arthritis, tumours, cancers, skin disorders, all kinds of backache, migraine, deafness, various phobias, diabetes, tension and stress.

As for the other 30 per cent, we cannot say exactly why the therapy does not work for them. As mentioned previously, they may simply not be ready for some reason: perhaps they do not fully accept that the therapy can help them, which is an important consideration. It is possible that at a later date, and with another clinic, the therapy might work. The failure to get a response in those people does not seem to bear any relationship to the seriousness of the disorder. There is one possibility – and it is nothing more than that – that may explain why the therapy does not work for some people. In order to explore this, let us look at the work of Dr Gertrude Schmeider of Radcliffe College in the USA and her experiment in 1942 into the possibility of the existence of extra-sensory perception (ESP). She asked the students whom she was about to test to say whether they believed in ESP. Those who did were classed as sheep and those who did not as goats. She then tested their ability to identify hidden cards, with interesting results. The sheep scored above average; more significantly, the goats scored well below average. The goats had either consciously or unconsciously 'cheated' in order to support their view (that ESP did not exist), but this showed up in their results. If they had scored at about average, there would have been nothing strange in the results. But they apparently used a perception they claimed they did not believe in to back up their belief that there was no such thing as ESP. In so doing, they showed just as much ESP as the sheep.

We are not suggesting that people who do not benefit from

bio-energy therapy are deliberately not getting better to prove that the therapy does not work. As we said, the people in the above experiment were not necessarily conscious of what they were doing. We just do not know the extent of the capabilities of the human mind. We merely offer the theory for what it is worth, that some people do not want to let go of their problem or disease, and attend bio-energy clinics wishing to remain as they are. This wish can be either conscious or unconscious.

PERSONAL EXPERIENCES

Some patients who attend the clinics have extremely bad energy blockages. When released, these energies have to be directed away from ourselves and the patient in a certain way. If we were to absorb those energies into our own energy fields, we would end up needing treatment. Conversely, when working with a patient who has a major depletion of energy in a certain part of their energy field, it is possible that we could be drained of our own energy and become weak and nauseous.

This brings us to another question about bio-energy therapy that patients often ask about. Is this released energy of any danger to other patients who are in the room? The short answer to this is 'no'. Once the released energy is outside the combined energy field of both the therapist and the patient, it goes back into the vast pool of energy that is all around us and poses no threat to any other person in the room. The reason we are able to say this with certainty is that we have sensitized our hands and are able to tell exactly where the energy goes when it is released.

When we first began treating patients, we were able to feel shock waves running up our arms when we released a patient's energy. The reason for this was that we had not fully learned how to deflect the energy away from the combined energy fields. We learned that the positioning of our bodies relative to the patient's body, combined with a series of hand movements, is the secret to diverting excess energy from where it might do harm. But we had other difficulties in the early days of administering the therapy, one of them being how to recognise when a person had a serious depletion of energy. Very ill patients with such a depletion can be very negative and this state can affect everybody in the room, including ourselves. We had to make sure that we had a positive attitude at all times and knew how to handle such situations. It was only through trial and error that we learned to do this and it is a knowledge that we pass on to the therapists who work with us.

As we developed the therapy, another thing we noticed was that our own energy fields became very sensitive at an energy level to everything around us. The more we became aware of this external energy, the more we were able to accomplish. This increased sensitivity can have its drawbacks, however. Initially, meeting people on the street or walking into a room where there were sick people could have a draining effect on us. We had to learn to cut off at that stage, to live a totally different way of life. In social circumstances, we had to be especially careful to ensure that we were not being 'drained' of our energy. (This feeling is similar to the experience of being in the company of somebody whom you find extremely boring. You will invariably say afterwards that the person has 'drained' you or you 'feel drained'. In terms of energy depletion, this is exactly what can happen.) It is a fact that most sick people, having sunk so far down that they cannot see any way out for themselves, become very selfish. In our experience, they can drain other people of their energy unconsciously. Sick people will clutch at anything if they think it can help them. Nonetheless, we have to be aware of what can happen, since we can be of little use to anyone if we need treatment ourselves.

Bio-energy therapy can be used to treat just about any disorder. The energy field of the patient contains the total make-up of the individual on a physical, mental, emotional and spiritual level. It carries all the necessary information for us to locate exactly where the illness lies at an energy level. In the case of a psychiatric disorder, for example, we can usually locate the problem in the area of the head, but in addition there may be other energy centres blocked which are nowhere near the head but which still affect a person's mental health. A blockage in the throat area may show up as a lack of concentration, which will colour the way a person looks at life. With bio-energy treatment, there is no reason why that person will not make a complete recovery.

The therapy also involves treating people in aspects other than the energy level. During treatment, we take time to talk with our patients. This can go a long way towards teasing out deep-rooted problems. This can be an aspect missing in a busy modern surgery, where the doctor simply does not have the time to sit and talk with patients. Many patients simply need to talk to someone about their problems – not necessarily an experienced counsellor, just another human being. We discovered this necessity when we realised the importance of getting people to recall when they first experienced their present disorder. In many cases, this regression was the key to their recovery.

Severe emotional shock can often led to an energy imbalance and subsequent illness. It is interesting to note that such shocks have also been linked to the development of cancer, with the disease surfacing some two years after the shock. If someone in the family or a very close friend has died, the patient may not have been able to grieve properly, which can lead to an energy blockage at the emotional level and later physical disorder. Even if they have grieved, it might be the case that they still have not accepted the death of a loved one. Patients have to be led back to the time when they first experienced the symptoms of their condition, so that the event which triggered it can be identified and dealt with. This is naturally an emotional experience and it should come as no surprise to learn that numerous patients have broken down and cried in a clinic as a result of the emotional release. This is not to suggest that the therapy is somehow a giant emotional free-for-all, where patients are invited to get everything off their chest. Far from it. But in order for the therapy to work, we found it necessary to develop the treatment in such a way as to allow our patients to talk freely, without any pressure and for as long as they need.

There is no guarantee with such traumatised patients that they will make a recovery in the immediate or even the long term. As with all patients, there are too many variables to be able to say with certainty who will recover and who will not. In cases of severe emotional trauma or stress, memory plays an important part. The energy imbalance may have been present for a long time and even when we balance the energy field it is possible that the residual memory will reprogramme the energy field when the treatment is finished. In such cases, we advise people to come back for further treatment until the memory has lost its power over the energy field. The memory left over from the trauma may have left an imprint at a very deep level in the mind and, in general, recovery in such cases is a gradual process, with the more traumatic aspects of the disorder lessening over a period.

We have noticed that when traumatised patients come to accept that the life energy does exist and that their disorder has to be tackled at this level, they can become well again. This in itself is a big step for a person who four or five days earlier had never even heard of such energies. Patients also come to understand that it may take some time for the benefits of the therapy to show up in their physical body. The length of time is different for everybody. Since people get sick at different rates, it is only natural that they should heal also at different rates. Some patients can be helped in a matters of minutes, while others may take many months.

There are cases where the amount of treatment a patient receives makes all the difference. We have treated people in one clinic and they have not benefitted at all, but a second or even a third clinic has been of enormous help. We have found that the key is the amount of treatment a person gets at the initial stage: the more treatment at the start, the better the potential results for that person. Again, we do not know why this is. We have had patients who have been treated successfully but who have reverted back to illness again after a period of time. This brings us to another question that people often ask about the therapy: how long does it last? Again, the answer is that we just do not know for sure. We do know, however, that we have treated patients years ago and that their disease or condition has not recurred. Conversely, we have treated patients successfully and in less than a couple of months they have suffered a relapse.

We can speculate as to why some patients regress and others do not on the basis of observations we have made. Patients who have been suffering from chronic illness have had an energy imbalance developing over maybe ten, twenty, even forty years. In some cases we know of, their home or work situation was stressful and full of pressures. Having treated such people successfully at a clinic, they then return to the very situation that caused their illness in the first place and, naturally enough, they have a relapse. We can only give general pointers to patients as to how they might look at their lives, even though we may be well aware of what might have caused their problems. But we cannot order them to change their lifestyle. In the final analysis, it is up to each person what they decide they want to do. We realise that actually doing something about their home or work situation may be troublesome in the short term, but there is simply no avoiding the hard decisions that must be made if they are to get better. As far as we are concerned in many of the cases where people had a recurrence of their illness, there was no other course for them to follow other than to review their life and to change it if they wished to remain healthy.

Thus we have learned that in many cases the apparent illness is not really the problem at all. We have trained long and hard at the therapy and have developed a knowledge, intuitive in part, which allows us to get straight to the heart of the matter on an energy level. We cannot state for a fact that the energy imbalance comes first, either through an emotional trauma or something else, and then the physical disorder manifests itself. What we can say is that an energy imbalance will lead to a physical disorder if it is not rectified and that a physical blow to the body received years earlier will show up at an energy level and may stay there unless it is treated.

Bio-energy therapy is a natural process and differs from certain other methods of helping sick people. We can teach people about the therapy and it is theoretically possible for every healthy person to administer it. However, not everyone is able to do so and this is another curious fact we have tried to explain. Perhaps in the same way that the therapy does not work for everyone, so too with administering it. Perhaps not everyone is ready to assume the role of therapist. There are certain basic requirements needed, including good health, compassion for human beings, both in general and in particular, and a willingness on the part of the therapist to impose a discipline on themselves in order to learn the techniques. Compassion, the ability to reach out and help those that are suffering, plays a crucial part in the therapist's make-up. This compassion and desire to help others must be without any motivation for self-advancement or reward. If the motives got mixed up with egotistical or materialistic reasons, it is quite possible that the therapy would not work.

When we talk about the necessity of having compassion in our work, this should not under any circumstances be confused with emotional attachment or personal involvement with patients. Such involvement is not a good idea. The compassion we are talking about is a general compassion for the human race and for life. This is not to say that we cannot treat members of our own family or close friends. We certainly can and the therapy will work just as well, if not better, on those for whom we care most.

Our training has involved learning much about ourselves and so developing a deep inner knowledge, which has added to our intuitive knowledge. We are continuously learning to pick up ever more sensitive energy fields and levels within the energy field itself, making us increasingly effective in helping people. The way we have developed the treatment in our clinics may perplex some people. For example, our training and development has led us to the view that to release blocked energy it is sometimes easier to remove it through the feet, regardless of where the blockage lies. In cases where patients have had severe migraine headaches, they may query this approach but once their pain has disappeared they no longer have any problems with the technique.

The basic objective of the therapy – to balance the human energy field so that the person being treated is healthier, more whole and more contented in their life – is easy to describe in words. Less easy to describe are the sensations of the subtle energies contained in the human energy field and how they are manipulated and changed so that patients can be helped. Different therapists use different words to describe these sensations and how they feel them in their hands. The end result, however, is the same, despite the differences in perception. It is, after all, thought, will and imagination that direct energy and decide where it goes and to what purpose.

All life forms share the same life energy and therefore the therapy can be applied universally. This allows a patient to tap an inner font of energy, strength and insight that is available to everyone. It is not necessary that people believe in the therapy in order to obtain positive and beneficial results, only that they are open to it. A certain degree of scepticism is not detrimental. One of the things we have noticed in our clinics is that some of the most successful results usually involve a psychological change in a patient and this change takes place despite the fact that the illness was physical in nature. Patients who have obtained positive results usually end up with a different perspective on life and illness. In these instances, the therapy has given them much more than just relief from physical trauma, pain and suffering.

We have come across cases where patients were resentful towards somebody (often a member of their family) and these feelings, whether on a conscious or unconscious level, have, in our view, played a crucial role in determining whether or not the therapy will work for them. Sometimes these feelings have been building up over many years and are hard to dislodge. Recovery is aided by the patient having a willingness, again either conscious or unconscious, to change perspective.

Patients who attend a clinic often say that they find the therapy very relaxing. The main reason for this is that patients tend to leave their worries behind them when they are being treated. The mind is concentrated on just one moment in time, the moment of treatment, and this does not allow other thoughts of the past or future to intrude. This state of mind is important for it allows the energies to flow freely and balance themselves. Negative thought patterns, related to unsuccessful treatments in the past for example, need to be eradicated so that a climate can be created in which the body's natural healing ability can take over. It is our job to ensure that this process continues to its natural conclusion.

Contrary to what many people would expect, chronically or terminally ill people often respond better and faster to the therapy than patients with less serious ailments. We do not give them a false hope. Numerous cases have shown that where there does not appear to be any change in the symptoms of the disease when a clinic is over, this is by no means the end of the story. We have treated people who have been given up for dead by others and they have lived. But hope of recovery has got to be balanced against the fact that the outcome of some diseases and disorders is death. As human beings, we must accept that there is a time to die and if that time has come, then the therapy has a role in helping people accept that fact and face death without fear and with a sense of inner peace and contentment. This is brought about through compassion and the reduction or elimination of pain. This is healing by another name.

When a patient dies, we have to be able to cope with this and understand that it is not a personal defeat. We have to be able to go back into the clinic the next day with the same sense of harmony and optimism, and administer the therapy. When we are working together, it is vital that we are able to help each other when problems arise. Everyone has off days during which the support and comfort of colleagues is needed. If that support is not forthcoming, as would be the case if we were in the work for the wrong reasons, then this would have a knock-on effect on the clinic and the positive results achieved to date.

Apart from having the right motivation, we also need a degree of physical stamina in order to last through a clinic. The continuous movements of our arms and hands involved in the manipulation of energy during the therapy can be quite tiring, but it is essential that the final energy sweep of the day is applied to the last patient with the same vigour and concentration as to the first. We also need to continue to develop the sensitivity in our hands since these are the main instruments we use to feel what is going on in the energy field and to direct the healing energies towards the patient. Successful application of the therapy involves being able to move around the contours of the energy field and feel it without hesitation, while maintaining a relaxed body position at the same time. Hands that are stiff with tension cannot feel the energy field properly and small blockages may go unnoticed. We perform a number of exercises to maintain this sensitivity (for example, opening and closing the hands whilst placing them under hot and cold running water alternatively), based on relaxing both the mind and body prior to a clinic. We need to take care of the hands, too, for example by wearing gloves to protect against blisters or cuts or extremes of weather.

Our own state of mind is important for the success of the therapy. We need to be relaxed during it and aware of our role as conduits only of the life energy, not as its source. Since this energy follows the intent or will of the therapist, it can affect not only the body of the patient, but also our own. The thoughts and intentions emanating from the human brain are made up of tiny electronic signals and these can interact with other more powerful energies around us. The energies of someone who is ill are striving to get back in balance and, through harmonising our intent and our action with that of nature, we can stimulate the healing process. This is what makes the therapy work, along with the strong desire of the patient to be well.

We work at a number of different levels in a clinic. With each passing day, different manipulations of energies may have to take place within a patient. After assessing the energy field initially, we clear the small blockages, then transfer energy into the depleted areas and finally balance the energy flow throughout the whole field. It may surprise people to know that this is the standard procedure no matter what physical symptoms are present. Depending on the patient and the requirements of a session, these various techniques will either be done separately or following one another or perhaps even all at once. An intuitive element is involved here and this varies from therapist to therapist. One person might decide to carry out all the actions simultaneously, whilst another might decide to do them separately. The eventual outcome will be the same. The decision as to how the therapy is administered is at the discretion of the therapist. The individuality of the patient is the overriding factor and focus of attention, not the illness itself.

For the initial diagnosis, it is easiest for us to pick up the energy field with our hands a few inches from the patient's body. We should not be so close that body heat and clothing give false readings, but we have found that the further away we go, the less easy it is to be accurate about the signals. The entire energy field must be assessed because we are looking for an imbalance which can lie anywhere within it. We do this scan of the energy field by passing our hands down the body, from the top of the head to the feet. (The latter are important because it is through them that many blockages will be released; if there is a blockage anywhere near the feet, it has to be cleared first.) We usually place one hand in front of the body and another behind, creating a polarity effect between the two hands which increases the strength of the signals we are receiving. Using this technique during the actual treatment of the patient also has the effect of increasing the flow of energy to the point where it is double that of just one hand. Placing both hands side by side in front of the body and moving them together downwards from the head is another technique which allows us to sense any imbalance between the right and left side of the energy field.

This initial assessment is usually done fairly quickly, taking about a minute or two, and involves much of our intuitive sense. Spending too long in the diagnosis can make us over-conscious of ourselves and therefore take away from our instinctive reactions, which often lead to the development of new and better techniques. While it is possible to explain much about bio-energy therapy, this area of instinct is harder to rationalise. Different therapists react differently and employ different techniques in their treatment of patients.

Everything that we do during the treatment of a patient can have an effect on their energy field. Thus we have to be careful, for example, that our hand movements are kept smooth. If they are not, the effect on the energy field can irritate the patient and they will not be relaxed and therefore the trust that needs to be built up between the parties may not materialise. If we move too quickly over the energy field, the patient may get an uncomfortable sensation on a physical level and may become slightly frightened. When scanning the energy field of a healthy person, we may feel it as being soft and warm, or as a very gentle vibration. It will feel comfortable, with no breaks in the free flow of energy. However, our hands register different sensations when working with sick people.

In general, there are four basic areas in which the energy field may become unbalanced and they account for 90 per cent of the people who attend our clinics. There are those people with small blockages in the energy field and those with large blockages; there are those with a depletion in the energy field and, finally, there are those with an imbalance of the whole energy field.

Blockages or depletions have the effect of breaking up the basic wholeness of a person, of fragmenting their being. When a blockage has been removed from a particular area, we find that the patient can take in more energy at that point simply because the blockage is gone. The most common way of releasing a blockage of energy, no matter where it occurs, is to take the built-up energy out through the patient's hands and feet. A small blockage can feel like a surge of heat or a slight pressure or heaviness in the hands. This sensation is common at the site of wounds or infections, or at the spot where surgery has recently taken place. Small blockages may also be located throughout the energy field, yet there may be no correlating physical problem at any of the sites. It is at this level that blockages can manifest themselves long before any physical illness is apparent. In some cases, having removed a light blockage, we may then discover an even bigger blockage beneath it which we were unable to feel before. To this end, patients need continuous assessment, not just on the first day of a clinic but throughout its four or five days. The patient's energy field starts to rebalance itself after treatment on the first day and needs continual monitoring as the energies are adjusted each day.

Large blockages are usually found near one of the seven major energy centres. Their effect is to block the free flow of energy running from the top of the head to the base of the spine and they must be removed before any energy is transferred to the patient. The physical symptoms of such blockages can show up in any part of the body. To our hands, such blockages manifest themselves as a coldness, a void or emptiness. Chronic diseases will usually be felt like this.

Energy depletion is often found at the site of a wound or infection. But it results in affecting more than just the immediate area: there is a debilitating effect on the whole person. Patients will have no energy for life and cannot summon up the will to allow their bodies to heal naturally. To our hands, these depletions feel like a pulling sensation or a hollowness. The area affected can sometimes give the impression of pulling in energy and, indeed, this is what happens when we start to work on the problem.

Depletions are nearly always revealed beneath blockages. This is explained by the fact that a blockage results in a stoppage of energy flow which, in turn, creates a depletion since no energy is getting in at that point. This reinforces the necessity for ongoing assessment of the energy field throughout a clinic.

Most imbalances are located around malfunctioning internal organs, such as the liver or kidneys. The aim of the therapy is to get the whole energy field in balance again so that the affected organ can begin to recover. There are cases where our treatment does not match the earlier medical treatment that the patient received. We may treat an area that appears far removed from the site of the illness. But when the patient's energy imbalance has been corrected and the symptoms and the illness disappear, then our treatment is validated. In other cases where the patient's doctor has been unable to find anything wrong, we find that the symptoms complained of in their physical body correspond roughly to the same area in their energy field. Hence, it is possible to treat a patient on an energy level even though medical science is unable to diagnose the complaint due to a lack of physical evidence.

In clinics, it is not unusual to have more than one therapist work on a patient at the same time. Occasionally this happens because it is necessary for one therapist to validate the assessment of another. Then some patients actually need two people working on them because their disorder demands it. For example, in cases where a blockage is very severe, two therapists might work on a patient in order to deflect the energy away from themselves. In the cases of severe depletions, two therapists working towards a common aim can help a patient much better and quicker.

Small blockages are cleared with downward sweeping movements of the hands from the top of the body towards the feet. When the therapist finds that there is what might best be described as 'static' sticking to their hands, they shake their hands in such a way as to get rid of it, in much the same way as a person would shake off water. If this static is not got rid of, it would dull the sensations reaching the hands as well as the flow of energy.

The visualisation process that goes on in the mind of the therapist during treatment is important. We have to visualise the flow of energy through our own energy field into that of the patient, all the while washing, cleansing and replenishing the affected part. Each therapist uses a personal set of symbols: it may be flowing water or a beam of light. Whatever vehicle is used, it is important to view oneself as the conduit of the energy, not the source of it. We are only the instruments through which the universal energy is drawn and projected. When we visualise the flow of the energy successfully, we always find that our own energies are replenished as well as those of the patients.

The amount of energy removed or given to a patient has to be carefully regulated. If too much energy is taken out while clearing a blockage, or put in while replenishing a depletion, a slight dizziness may be experienced by the patient. But generally, the flow of energy into or out of a patient will stop automatically, as there seems to be a limit. The energy field itself regulates this and once it happens, treatment is stopped for that day. We must be sensitive to these signals and know when to stop. But even if the energy field has been overcharged slightly, the symptoms will last for only a few moments while the patient sits or lies still.

When releasing large blockages, we have to visualise the energy going deeply into the blocked energy centres. Our will and intent in directing the energy releases the blockage. The solar plexus, or stomach, is often affected by blockages, making it one of the most vulnerable areas of the body. Anxiety, tension and emotional stress can build up in this area and result in a range of physical disorders, such as ulcers. The area close to the kidneys is also vulnerable to blockages, especially if patients are on antibiotics of any sort. When we are treating these areas, visualisation of the energy flow, especially in terms of colour (see Chapter 4), is important. In the two examples above, dark blue is significant because of its soothing and healing qualities.

Major blockages are always released early on in the treatment. If this were not done, the transferring of energy and the unblocking of smaller blockages would be hampered. A large blockage can quickly be turned into a small blockage and treated almost at once. In the case of chronic illness, several treatments may be needed to remove a large blockage. When the patient leaves a clinic, the healing process has been set in motion at a deep level and will continue to work, smashing negative thought patterns and habits associated with the disorder.

The average treatment per patient at a clinic in any one day is about fifteen minutes. Children are generally far more sensitive than adults and take a much shorter time, perhaps five minutes or so. A young baby can take just a minute. Patients who have been treated should rest and relax for about half an hour afterwards, whether they feel they need to or not. This has the effect of allowing the energies to become balanced in a relaxed atmosphere following the therapy.

People respond differently to the therapy and sometimes it is not really practicable to try and determine the length of the treatment in terms of minutes. Some people may have received sufficient treatment in one minute of one session, whereas another person might take half an hour. There is no hard and fast rule about this. The basis of the treatment is that when we feel that a particular patient has had enough treatment for that session, then that, in effect, is enough. As soon as the thought crosses our minds, then the treatment has as good as stopped. How we arrive at this thought is hard to explain. We will get a feeling in the energy field to indicate to us that the therapy should be terminated for that day. Even when we are in doubt as to whether to continue treating the patient, we usually stop anyway since that small doubt will diminish the effectiveness of the therapy. It is therefore a combination of what we feel in our hands together with our intuition that dictates the length of treatment. If we are over-anxious about the potential success of the therapy as we work, this expectation will actually interfere with the process and distract us.

Another thing we must guard against while we work is a bias against any particular patient in a clinic. This again will have the effect of breaking our concentration and reducing the effectiveness of the treatment. No matter how difficult this may be or how implausible it may sound, we have to look on individual patients as part of a greater humanity; we must remember that in treating the individual, we are treating part of the human race and so we must constantly refer back to our motivation as therapists.

One of the most important aspects for us is feedback from our patients. When a patient tells us what they are feeling, when and where they are feeling it, this confirms our diagnosis of their energy field. It is also desirable that patients return to clinics for regular checkups in which their energy field can be balanced continually, rather than waiting for a manifestation of the disorder to reappear. Patients themselves will know when the treatment should cease altogether since they will feel it within themselves. At that point, the patient is fully recovered and is able to balance their own energy field without any outside help.

In general, longer and longer periods of time between each clinic indicate that the patient is on the road to recovery. In the case of asthma, for example, people who are treated on a regular basis tend to get fewer attacks and less severe ones than an asthma-sufferer who comes to the clinic only when they are having particularly bad attacks. When patients attend the clinic while they are manifesting the more severe symptoms of their condition, it is then that the dramatic examples of healing occur. This is simply because their condition is such that any healing which takes place, no matter how small, becomes apparent immediately.

Patients in general do not experience a gradual diminution of their disorder. What usually tends to happen is that they improve by leaps and bounds, and then there follows a period in which there is no change or even a worsening of the condition; this is followed by another significant improvement. Treatment over a period has a deep and more lasting effect. Patients recover more than just their physical health: they are given back their freedom and independence, and are no longer the slave of their illness.

This account of some of the more important aspects of the workings of bio-energy therapy in our clinics is our honest impression of what we do. It is difficult to put into words everything that happens in a clinic and because we are learning more and more with each passing week, the story is not yet over. We have learned enough to know our own limitations at present, yet we also know that there is no limit to what we can learn.

CHAPTER 6

Other Factors Affecting Good Health

Many patients who attend our bio-energy clinics, referred to us by doctors, are on medication, often for a long period. Treating such patients over the years has caused us to take a critical look at the medical profession and its habit of prescribing drugs. One of the most alarming facts we discovered was that few people are told about the potential side-effects that many drugs possess.

As bio-energy therapists, we have no medical qualifications nor are we authorities in any way on the subject of drugs. We can, however, speak from our experience in clinics and describe the almost textbook-like list of side-effects complained of by the people we treat. These side-effects impinge so greatly on bio-energy therapy and affect it so adversely that we were forced to monitor these effects and collect data, published by the medical profession itself, on various drugs. Thus, most of our research comes from secondary (published) sources, with the important exceptions of the people we know who are on certain medication and who are suffering the exact side-effects anticipated in the medical texts.

There is an extraordinary degree of ignorance regarding the side-effects of drugs. We have found that patients coming to us have been denied even the most basic knowledge about the possible side-effects of the medication they are taking. In order to redress this balance, we bring medical textbooks into our clinics and patients who want to find out about their medication can do so. We have come across cases where patients have been given injections by their GP but have been refused the name of the drug. We have found that the medical profession, in general, treats patients as if they have no right to know. Patients have basic rights, and one of those rights is to be told what damage, if any, prescribed and legal medication will cause their health.

Our training in bio-energy therapy had not prepared us for these issues, since neither the practitioners of the therapy in the East nor Domancic of Yugoslavia, who introduced the therapy to the West, had a similar drug culture with which to contend. Initially, we were amazed at the willingness of people to take whatever was prescribed without question. (This is changing in recent years due to the many documented reports on the dangerous side-effects of many drugs.) We concluded that people have generally been lulled into a passive state of mind in which acceptance is a way of life. This attitude is deeply ingrained from an early age.

As babies our basic needs are taken care of. We continue on to school, where institutions tell us what to do and when to do it. Then we drift into a job, if we are lucky, where again we are 'managed'. All through our lives, we are being discouraged from thinking for ourselves. In short, in the face of such prolonged and sustained brainwashing, we conform. We become unused to exercising freedom in our own lives. Our passivity manifests itself in many ways, from such apparently innocuous ways as waiting in queues to the more important ways of taking any drug prescribed by a doctor, generally in an unquestioning fashion.

In this passive type of lifestyle, we are running on automatic. This habit is absolutely disastrous for us. Our energy levels are determined by the subconscious mind. When we are living in what could be termed a half-sleeping state, it is only in the case of an emergency that we will really wake up and perform at capacity. At this point, our consciousness is very much awake and we get a sense of control back into our lives.

When we begin to look at the nature of illness and how disease is dealt with in the world, we have to look at modern medicine with a somewhat sceptical eye. A person's will and energy often degenerate as they fall ill. Sick people are usually not in a position to fight back. The first thing that needs to be said is that there appears to be a tendency on the part of doctors to prescribe drugs as a first, rather than a last resort. Why is this so? Admittedly, there are many doctors who are so busy that the only way they can have any kind of normal life and normal working hours is to release patients as quickly as they can from their surgeries; the quickest way of doing this often involves writing a prescription. This is rather less the fault of doctors than the system that has put them into that position. The kindest interpretation we can put on this type of behaviour is that doctors are overworked; a less kind interpretation suggests that there is something a little more sinister going on.

There is no doubt, based on the evidence of doctors' patients who attend our bio-energy clinics, that some doctors are little more than salesmen on behalf of the drug companies. There have been few investigations into how these doctors actually get their drugs from the drug companies and what pressures, if any, are put on them to prescribe drugs in general or certain drugs in particular.

The World Health Organization (WHO) has pointed out on numerous occasions that there are well in excess of 24,000 individual drugs available in the world today, of which only about 200 are necessary for the treatment of the major ailments from which we suffer. The question has to be asked why so many drugs are being produced and marketed. In our opinion, the answer is that these drugs are not being produced in order to help sick people exclusively, but in order to further the profits of the multinational drug companies.

The world in which we live is consuming more than 120 billion dollars worth of drugs each year, according to the WHO. The research and development departments of the major drug companies are well funded and well staffed, yet dangerous drugs still find their way onto the market and have to be withdrawn, a process which can sometimes take years. What is most frightening about this is that people who have taken a drug that has subsequently been withdrawn may be completely ignorant of its possible side-effects. A recent example will serve to illustrate.

From the 1950s right through the 1970s, thousands of women all over the world were prescribed the synthetic hormone DES. Its function was to prevent miscarriages and premature births, and it was marketed under 100 different brand names. Press reports in Ireland during late 1990 suggested that Irish women *may* have taken the drug; it was stated that in 1981 in Holland, it was presumed that no Dutch women had taken DES but following publicity some 200,000 people came forward to state that they had taken it under prescription. It was later found that the daughters of women who had taken this drug could be infertile and/or suffer from certain types of cancer. At the time of writing, the Department of Health in Ireland has issued questionnaires to GPs around the country and it may be that about 1000 women were prescribed DES.

Another frequent problem we have encountered in our work is overprescription of drugs, especially tranquillisers. This has long been a matter of concern to the medical profession also. In 1984, for example, valium was the third most commonly prescribed drug in Ireland under the General Medical Scheme, according to Department of Health figures; in that year, 332,797 prescriptions were issued for valium. The Committee for the Review of Medicines stated that tranquillisers were overprescribed, particularly in relation to the elderly and to children.

In July 1988, it emerged that 308,960 of the one million or so prescriptions issued on the Health Service the previous year were for what could be termed 'addictive drugs', with a total cost of £257,000. The National Drugs Advisory Board added its voice of concern, saying that the number of prescriptions for tranquillisers was far too high. A leading medical practitioner estimated that 22,000 people were addicted to legally prescribed drugs in Ireland and that the prescription rate for such drugs was rising rapidly.

This state of affairs does not take into account the possible side-effects of drugs, apart from their addictive nature. In 1988 (the latest figures available at the time of writing), the National Drugs Advisory Board noted in its annual report that 23 deaths were associated with legally prescribed medicines; 3 of these were due to wilful overdose, 4 were not drug-related and 2 were 'only improbably' related to drug therapy. The same report noted that there were 1,861 side-effects concerning a total of 1,031 patients monitored.

These figures do not necessarily represent the full picture. We have come across many patients in our clinics who are suffering from the side-effects of medication and who have never informed their doctor or the National Drugs Advisory Board. The profound level of ignorance found among patients about drugs is not necessarily their fault. Many are simply afraid to question their GP, while others who have asked were refused the necessary information. In our opinion, the basic 'right to know' about prescribed drugs and their possible side-effects is being denied patients on an ongoing basis by a significant number of GPs and specialists.

The side-effects noted in the annual report of the National Drugs Advisory Board, quoted above, spanned a wide range of drugs which affected every system in the body. Some of the side-effects noted include urinary retention, drowsiness, lethargy, weakness, dizziness, respiratory arrest, coma, neck spasm, paralysis, paranoia, rigidity, nausea, lightheadedness, grinding of teeth, hallucinations, nightmares, rashes, thirst, mouth-dryness, confusion, vomiting, tremor, foetal distress, diarrhoea, exacerbation of epilepsy, abdominal pain, headache, flushing, gastritis, emotional upset, taste-perversion, increased sweating, palpitations, restlessness, abnormal vision, hypertension, epileptic seizures, shock, unconsciousness, duodenal ulcer, anorexia, constipation, hot flushes, wheeze, bleeding ulcer, flatulence, peptic ulcer, collapse, abnormal liver function, anxiety, disorientation, vertigo, colitis, malaise, kidney failure, tongue-swelling, oedema, hand blisters, swollen fingers, chest pain, impotence, blurred vision, heart failure, personality change, agitation, raving, vivid dreams, sore gums, cough, cramps, dermatitis, gout, nasal congestion, bowel obstruction, tiredness, facial pain, sensation of faintness, back pain, breast-tenderness, behavioural changes, irritability, migraine, weight gain, aggression, depression and death.

We are not, of course, suggesting that everyone who takes a drug will have any of these side-effects. These are merely the *potential* side-effects in *some* people of a wide range of drugs and we should add that some people appear to be more susceptible to side-effects than others.

The side-effects listed above are mostly short-term, but there has been very little research published, or easily available, into the long-term side-effects of drugs. A leading doctor who specialises in 'Stage One Clinical Trials' of drugs (drugs that are tested for the first time on volunteers) has been reported as saying that records are not kept for more than 5 years. If this is the case with the testing of new drugs, then it is natural to assume that in the case of more acceptable or established drugs there is less urgency about ongoing monitoring over the longer term.

None of this is to suggest that drugs have no place in the treatment of disease; on the contrary, drugs have a most important part to play. In the area of surgery, for example, drugs have given immense and immeasurable relief to people who would otherwise have suffered great pain. The issue here is about the prevalent and increasing dependence on drugs and their administration. We are also concerned that drugs should not mask an illness or be used to the exclusion of other forms of therapy which may be more effective.

Drug companies may argue that they are in the business of helping people, but the manufacture of drugs on the scale that is taking place would seem to suggest that there is something more than love of the human race involved here. Reports constantly emanating from the United States Securities and Exchange Commission indicate that drug companies are not shy when it comes to making questionable payments to governments, corporations, doctors and ordinary lay people in order to promote themselves. More than seventy companies were accused by the Commission of offering bribes to governments and companies in order to get a foothold in the marketplace in the early 1970s. These companies operated worldwide; almost half of them had a presence of one sort or another in Ireland.

Apart from their international operations, drug companies have been known to act in a quesionable manner at both a national and a local level. The relationship between the medical profession and the drug companies is one that needs examining if we are to understand why patients are prescribed drugs on such a widespread scale. Drug companies depend on doctors to promote their products. They are known to help out doctors and consultants when requested and sometimes when not requested. Medical seminars, meetings and international conferences are all helped greatly by donations or sponsorships from drug companies. In turn, it is only natural that some doctors may be well disposed towards the products of such companies. In Ireland alone, the drug business is worth up to £170 million a year; one-third of this accounts for the General Medical Scheme, according to the Department of Health.

There have been many examples of members of the medical profession going on junkets around the world at the expense of various drug companies which purport to be demonstrating some new wonder drug. As far back as 1978 a drug company sponsored two chairs of medicine at an Irish university, worth £60,000 spread over five years. Two doctors took up the positions. Three years later a Cork pharmacist alleged that the same drug company was paying two hospitals in the Southern Health Board region to administer a drug not yet approved by the National Drugs Advisory Board. He stated that neither he nor his colleagues considered that the drug in question was as effective as other drugs manufactured by other drug companies and which were used for the treatment of the same condition. (It should be noted that at the time it *was* permissible for certain hospitals to carry out clinical trials on new or semi-new drugs, so that this case would not necessarily have had to be passed by the National Drugs Advisory Board.) It then came to light that the same drug company had taken a group of Irish doctors abroad to see the working of the drug at first hand and that in fact four Irish hospitals had agreed to administer it to their patients. Doctors were paid £10 to £12 per patient to carry out this type of testing. This drug was removed from the market in 1983. This happened immediately prior to the publication of a British report which indicated that 330 cases of serious side effects had been reported, including four deaths, as a result of that particular drug. By that time about 200,000 people in Ireland and Europe had been given the drug. There has been no monitoring of the long-term effects if any of these cases.

The idea that there is something called a 'new drug' is open to question. In fact, the WHO has stated that in the past two decades, there have been less than 6 'new' drugs available, in the real sense of the word. Most 'new' drugs that come on the market are simply reformulations of old drugs. Up to 50 such 'new' drugs appear each year in Ireland, while about a dozen are withdrawn for various reasons, including serious side-effects or uselessness. The 'new' drug is launched when the 16-year patent runs out and the company needs to hold onto its market share. The hard sell by the drug companies means that a high percentage of their budget is put into promotion and the persuasion of doctors to their point of view. Unlike in the UK, there is no limit on the amount of money a company can spend on promotion in Ireland. This can be put into perspective when one considers the fact that there is one sales representative from the drug companies for every eight GPs in Ireland.

The drug companies appear to aim their strategy at those areas in which there are the greatest amount of sufferers – and therefore the greatest amount of money to be made. Because there is much competition between the companies for a slice of the Irish £170 million legal drugs market, it is worth putting the effort into 'cultivating' doctors who will promote their products. There are even companies which specialise in telling the drug companies how much each particular market (or sickness area, as it were) is worth. This is normal enough business practice, but is it an ethical way of dealing with people who are ill?

There are more than 2,500 GPs and consultants in Ireland. On average, each can get a call four times a year from every drug company. Doctors who agree to prescribe and monitor new drugs for the drug companies get paid for the service. There is no investigation of such doctors in Ireland, unlike in the USA where the Food and Drugs Administration monitor drugs carefully. The drug companies, while not employing doctors directly, do engage and pay medical consultants. It also has to be said that the drug companies, although they are the initiators in all this, do get 'begging letters' from doctors seeking money for meetings or projects in which they are currently engaged. We know this is so because doctors themselves have told us.

In order to pinpoint exactly where the medical profession is going wrong, it is worth looking at one specific area – allergies. One of the major problems with medicine is that disorders which fit into a certain pattern are diagnosed as certain diseases and are treated accordingly. There have been numerous cases of wrong diagnosis, where people have been taking medication for a disorder which they do not actually have. Allergies, particularly in the chemical category, are among the most common ailments that suffer from wrong diagnosis.

There has been a chemical explosion over the last 50 years or so which has placed human beings in contact with hundreds of artificially created chemicals. The long-term effects, if any, of such an intake of chemicals are as yet unknown, since the 'ingestion' period has been over only a relatively short timescale. The average Irish person takes 5lb of chemicals into his or her body each year; the average American is subjected to 9lb. These figures are not surprising when one considers that an ordinary loaf of bread these days contains no less than 48 chemicals.

One of the most common allergies today in children is hyperactivity. The general symptoms have been well recorded ('grasshopper'-type mind and lack of concentration) and are often directly attributable to diet. The condition can be totally reversed: various foods, such as dairy products and food colourings, are usually found to be the main culprits.

Studies conducted on allergies in Britain show that wrong diagnosis or a failure to diagnose an allergy can not only have the effect of physical pain and trauma, but also impose a heavy financial burden on the sufferer. Alison Bunnin's research into food allergies was published in 1989 under the title *The Career of the Food Allergy Sufferer*. The economic costs of food allergy, among other things, was scientifically broken down and, although the results obtained pertain to Britain, there is no reason to suppose that the figures would not relate to Ireland given the similarity of lifestyle and diet. For 30 allergy sufferers, the total cost of their affliction was Stg£279,300 before the allergy was diagnosed: there was £6,800 paid out for visits to the doctor, £27,200 in visits to State hospital out-patients departments and £39,900 in visits to in-patient departments, £17,500 in National Health Service drugs, £8,100 in private treatment, £155,400 in loss of earnings and £24,400 in government benefits. After the allergy was diagnosed and corrective action taken, the cost for these same 30 people went down to Stg£86,500, broken down as follows: £500 for visits to the doctor, £6,000 for out-patients services, nothing for in-patients services, £6,800 for National Health Service drugs, £43,200 for private treatment, £15,100 for loss of earnings and £14,900 for government benefits. By any stretch of the imagination, the financial savings are considerable, apart altogether from relieving the stress of the illness and handing people back their independence and dignity.

Bunnin's research highlighted other interesting observations on allergy sufferers. She identified five different stages of the illness: first came the stage in which people were bewildered at what was happening to them and this was often accompanied by a severe problem with the doctor/patient relationship; next, they made some sort of breakthrough; then, they experimented with different sorts of treatments; then, they learned to live with the allergy; and, finally, they reached the stage of looking beyond their illness and giving advice to others. She also noted that as people progressed through these stages, they developed a sense of identity as food allergy sufferers. In many instances, the allergy was discovered by chance. She concluded that perhaps the reason for this was that sufferers were getting less attention than they might do if their condition was life-threatening.

While there has been little research done in Ireland in the area of wrong diagnosis, it is at least arguable that, like allergy sufferers, there are many people around who are being treated incorrectly for various conditions following incorrect diagnosis.

SOME DRUGS AND THEIR SIDE-EFFECTS

It has been our experience that many of the people who attend bio-energy clinics, often on referral from their own GPs or specialists, are on medication of one kind or another. Frequently, they are on a range of drugs, since the side-effects of one drug often need to be counteracted by another. Some people know that the drugs they are taking cause serious side-effects, whereas others are totally unaware of this possibility. It has to be said, however, that many people who come to our clinics are on drugs that are doing them more harm than good. Until such time as the medical profession address the issue of the drug culture in their treatment of sick people, there is little chance of achieving anything more lasting than a quick 'fix' or the suppression of symptoms.

It is an undisputed fact that every drug has a side-effect, ranging from mild discomfort to sudden death. The brand names discussed below were picked at random from the 10,000 pharmaceutical products which are currently available in Ireland. The side-effects themselves can also be gleaned from a number of sources, all of which the medical profession have ready access to. Probably the most recently available is the *MIMS Directory*, which every doctor in the country gets. There is also the 'bible' of the chemical industry, the *Martindale Pharmacopaeia*, one of the world's most comprehensive sources of information on drugs in a single volume. Various medical journals will also, from time to time, carry reports on the side-effects of particular drugs. It should be noted that for each brand name mentioned, there are many others which could easily be substituted.

Cimeldine and Tagamet are two brand names of what are known as H2 blockers, whose function is to reduce acid secretion to very low levels. Both are supposed to be dispensed on a once-off basis. Both contain a drug known as 'cimetidine' which can produce such serious side-effects as diarrhoea, muscle pain, dizziness, occasional skin rashes and occasional reversible confusable states, especially in elderly or seriously ill patients. Other side-effects which have been noted from time to time include allergy, gynaecomastia, reversible changes in liver function values, fever interstitial nephritis, acute pancreatitis, cardiac arrhythmias and loss of libido.

Cimetidine also produces more specific side-effects in individual patients. For example, 5 patients developed a severe arthritic condition when they were given the drug; severe arrhythmias, fatal in one case, were noted in 2 cases; another patient developed hair loss; and 23 men became impotent. All the side-effects were reversed when the drug was discontinued.

Deseril is the brand name of an antidiarrhoeal drug. The medical profession are informed of the side-effects of this preparation, which contains 'methysergide'. These include nausea and other gastric disturbances, drowsiness, dizziness, oedema, arterial spasm, and retroperitoneal, pleural and heart valve fibrosis. There are also patients with certain conditions who should not be given this drug: such conditions include pregnancy, lactation, severe hypertension, oedema, pulmonary or collagen disorders, cardiac disease, impaired renal or hepatic function, cachexia, sepsis or peptic ulcer, and coronary, peripheral or occlusive vascular disease.

Navidrex-K is one of the 42 diuretic drugs currently available on the market. It contains 'cyclopenthiazide' and its side-effects are listed as rash, photosensitivity, blood dyscrasias, gout, fatigue, nausea, headache, dizziness, postural hypotension, cardiac arrhythmias and sometimes (but rarely) jaundice. The list continues, with allergies, skin rashes, thirst, epigastric pain, anorexia, gastric irritation, vomiting, diarrhoea, constipation, muscle spasm, weakness, inflammation of the salivary gland, loss of libido and paraesthesia

In the case of the cardiovascular system, there is a range of drugs available. It will come as no surprise that most of the major drug companies compete with each other for a share of this market, which in Ireland is a particularly lucrative one due to the high incidence of heart disease. *Sinthrome*, for example, is a drug that is prescribed. It contains 'nicoumalone' and is not recommended for children. The noted adverse reactions include haemorrhage, allergies, liver damage, reversible alcopecia, sometimes nausea, anorexia, headache and skin necrosis.

Accupro is a brand name containing the drug 'quinapril'. This can have serious side-effects including headache, dizziness, rhinitis, cough, upper respiratory tract infections, fatigue, nausea, dyspepsia, malagia, chest pain, abdominal pain, angioedema and hypotension. If hypotension occurs, it is recommended that treatment be stopped immediately. Like many other drugs, *Accupro* is meant to be a once-off prescription, unless specific instructions are issued to the contrary.

Xylocard is another brand product containing 'lignocaine hydrochloride'. This is a white crystalline odourless powder with a slightly bitter numbing taste that makes it useful as a local anaesthetic. It has a rapid action when injected and spreads throughout the surrounding tissues. Its side-effects have been noted to include agitation, drowsiness, disorientation, blurred vision, euphoria, tremor, convulsions, nausea, pallor, cold sweat, respiratory depression, fall in blood pressure, bradycardia and cardiac arrest. The drug is not recommended for children. A survey by the Boston Collaborative Drug Surveillance Program, which monitored 750 patients who had been given this drug, noted that 47 suffered adverse reactions; the condition of 12 of these 47 people was considered life-threatening.

Nif-Ten, containing 'atenolol', is a drug used in the treatment of angina. Again, it is not recommended for children. Side-effects include flushing, headache, fatigue, dizziness, nausea, dry eyes, skin rash, oedema, hypersensitivity type jaundice and, in rare cases, gingival hyperplasia. There are further side-effects of this drug, such as vomiting, diarrhoea, bradycardia, congestive heart failure, heart block, hypotension, cold extremities, Raynaud's phenomenon and paraethesia. The central nervous system can also be affected: depression, hallucinations and disturbances of sleep and vision can all occur. Blood disorders and skin rashes are other problems associated with this drug, as are constipation, fluid retention, weight gain, muscle cramps and dry mouth. Even small doses can have severe effects. Other drugs can be taken to counteract these, but they, in turn, have their own side-effects, so the whole problem is cumulative.

Dopagen contains 'methyldopa' whose side-effects have been noted to include sedation, headache, bradycardia, nasal congestion, dry mouth, gastrointestinal upset, hypotension, arthralgia, myalgia, sexual dysfunction, gynaecomastia, and Parkinsonism.

Incidentally, the most common side-effect of many drugs is headache. In order to cure this, the common *Aspirin* is the most used drug. Its side-effects include nausea, dyspepsia and vomiting, while irritation of the gastric mucosa with erosion, ulceration, haematemesis and melaena may also occur. About 70 per cent of people who take aspirin also suffer a slight blood loss. Certain people suffering from asthma can suffer various side-effects which can be fatal.

For circulatory disorders, *Stromba*, containing 'stanozolol', is sometimes prescribed. It is supposed to be dispensed once only and if a repeat is specified, that repeat is again a once-off. Side-effects include hepatotoxicity, virilisation in women and pre-pubertal children, fluid retention, dyspepsia, cramps and headache.

Hypnotics that act on the central nervous system are also popular. Many of these are household names. *Mogadon*, containing 'nitrazepam', is recommended as a once-off prescription. It is intended for the short-term treatment of insomnia and in cases where daytime sedation is acceptable. Basically it is a heavy-duty tranquilliser. Judgement and dexterity may be impaired as a result of taking this drug, but this is to be expected since its stated side-effects include drowsiness, light-headedness, ataxia, confusion, vertigo, gastric disturbances, abnormal psychological reactions, visual disturbances, skin rash, urinary retention, changes in libido, and sometimes blood disorders and jaundice. There is a risk of addiction to this drug, depending on the dosage and length of treatment.

There are many drugs available for the relief of severe anxiety, but they are not recommended to be taken for more than two to four weeks. One of these is a controlled drug under the Misuse of Drugs Act, Ireland: *Sodium Amytal*, containing 'amylobarbitone sodium', has precisely the same side-effects as *Mogadon*.

In order to control the more acute symptoms of schizophrenia, there is a host of drugs available. One is *Lexotan*, containing 'bromazepam'. This drug will interact with alcohol and other drugs, with adverse side-effects including spasms of the eye, face, neck and back, restlessness of the limbs, rigidity and tremoring, dry mouth, nasal stuffiness, difficulty in micturition, tachycardia, constipation, blurring of vision, hypotension, weight gain, impotence, galactorrheoa, hypothermia, gynaecomastia, amenorrhoea, benign obstructive jaundice, blood dyscrasias and dermatitis, ECG irregularities, drowsiness, lethargy, fatigue and epileptiform seizures.

The antidepressant *Prozac* contains 'fluoxetine'. This drug caused a storm in 1990 when it was found that it was still being prescribed despite the serious medical doubts expressed about it. Its side-effects included asthenia, fever, nausea, diarrhoea, dry mouth, appetite loss, dyspepsia, headache, nervousness, insomnia, drowsiness, anxiety, tremor, dizziness, fatigue, decreased libido, pharyngitis, dyspnoea, rash, convulsions, hallucinations, psychosis, hypomania and mania.

Tegretol is an anticonvulsant which contains 'carbamazepine'. It is prescribed mainly for epilepsy and has a range of reported side-effects, including gastric upset, diplopia, dry mouth, drowsiness, oedema, hypoatraemia, blood dyscrasias, rashes, acute kidney failure and cholestatic jaundice.

Six months is the recommended dosage time.

Brocadopa is a drug, recommended for once-off usage, containing 'levodopa'. It is prescribed for Parkinsonism and has been reported as causing nausea, vomiting, anorexia, postural hypotension, involuntary movements, cardiac and central nervous system disturbances, and urine discolouration.

Nurofen is an analgesic, containing 'Ibuprofen'. It is not recommended for children and the side-effects reported in adults include dyspepsia, gastric bleeding, rash and sometimes thrombocytopenia.

Ponstan, containing 'mefenamic', is a drug that is supposed to be given for 6 months only. It is given for pain associated with rheumatoid arthritis. The side-effects that have been reported include diarrhoea, skin rash, kidney problems and thrombocytopenia.

Voltarol is another drug prescribed for gout and recommended to be taken for 6 months only. It contains 'diclofenac sodium', whose side-effects have been reported as including transient epigastric pain, nausea, headache, rash, oedema, sometimes gastric bleeding, peptic ulcer and abnormalities of the kidney and liver functions.

In the area of hormone related drugs, which includes contraceptives, *Depo-Provera*, containing 'medroxy-progesterone acetate', is still on the market despite all the controversy surrounding it. In the case of continuous treatment, one side-effect has been transient infertility. Other side-effects include irregular, prolonged or heavy vaginal bleeding during the first two or three cycles, back pain, weight gain and fluid retention.

In the area of thyroid drugs, *Eltroxin*, containing 'thyroxine sodium', has various side-effects which include arrhythmias, anginal pain, tachycardia, muscle cramps, headache, restlessness, excitability, flushing, sweating, diarrhoea and excessive weight loss.

In the case of urinary tract infections, *Negram*, with 'nalidixic acid', is commonly prescribed. Side-effects noted have included gastric and visual disturbances, skin rashes, blood dyscrasias and convulsions. Another drug used on the urinary system is *Doralese,* containing 'indoramin'. Initially, a dose of this can cause drowsiness or sedation; other side-effects include dry mouth, nasal congestion, weight gain, dizziness, retrograde ejaculation, depression, sleep disturbances and vivid dreams.

This list of drugs is just a random selection available in Ireland at the time of writing. The specific side-effects have been taken from reputable medical sources which the medical profession uses. The point of listing all the various side-effects is not to frighten people, but rather to make people aware that drugs *do* have side-effects, sometimes serious ones, and that people have a right to know about these in advance. There is a clear responsibility on the part of the medical profession who prescribe the drugs to inform people of the possible dangers.

Once again, it is important that we reiterate our belief that drugs do have a part to play in the treatment of illness and pain. It is equally important, however, to repeat that the part drugs play in the health of an individual should not be to the exclusion of all other forms of treatment, including bio-energy. Our present world, at least in the West, is steeped in a drug culture and many sick people are like addicts, totally dependent on their drugs, with little personal choice in the matter. The time has come to call a halt to this. It is in the long-term interests of the medical profession to begin to examine this whole area. It could be a matter of life and death for their patients that they do this sooner rather than later.

CHAPTER 7

Testimonials from Patients

❁

Many many patients have benefitted greatly from attending a bio-energy clinic. As a result, we have received hundreds of testimonials from former patients over the past number of years. We print a selection below, some of them taken especially for this book in the latter part of 1990.

Cathleen Reilly, Claremorris, Co. Mayo

I had a bad back for 21 years. A year ago, I heard about bio-energy. I was literally crippled and I would go to the doctor and get injections and then the pain would come back again. I would be bent over for days. I couldn't do anything. I couldn't walk and the pain was excruciating. So I went to the bio-energy clinic and since then, I haven't had to take a tablet or anything. At the clinic, they did the usual massage and the therapy as well. The pain bothered me a bit after that again, but I went for more treatment again and it was fine.

My husband was also very ill. This time last year he ended up in hospital with what we thought was a heart attack. We later discovered that it wasn't a heart attack; he had a virus of the heart muscle. He was very weak and couldn't walk, and he was brought into the bio-energy clinic in Knock in October 1989. He literally couldn't stand up.

My husband is still attending the cardiologist. The last ECG he had was very good and the heart was three-fifths back to normal. He is in great form. And I was bad myself looking at him, because of the strain of it all. I was really worried. I'm convinced it's as a result of the bio-energy therapy that he's still alive.

John Ivors, Kiltimagh, Co. Mayo

It was five years ago when I was out in the garden and I got a dizziness. I was using a wheelbarrow and I thought the barrow was veering away from me, but I was actually going away from the barrow. I went to my doctor and he told me it was vertigo.

I wasn't getting any better. It was nerve racking at the time and there was a continuous buzz right into my left ear. The buzz always came off a voice into my ear and it was the same with television. I went to a specialist in Galway and he examined me and all he could say was that it was my past work that had caused the damage. I used to work with jackhammers in England years ago, long before there was any protection. In social situations, if people asked me a question, my wife used to have to answer for me. I couldn't hear anything in my left ear for five years. The doctors told me that there was no disease or anything there; they were sorry, but they could do nothing for me. That was it.

I came to the bio-energy clinic and I didn't notice anything on the first day. But on the second day, the buzz had gone and the hearing was improving. It was completely better by the last day. I had friends also who came to the clinic and we knew that they were better by coming here. I half understand the explanations for the therapy and how it works. I found the explanations helpful.

I can imagine how they can detect this breach in energy around your body. I could feel it when they were working on me. The therapist brought me up there to the corner and was at me for some time and that was the longest session I had. They really worked on the ear and after that I know myself they cured it.

Dick Wiseman, Rathmore, Co. Kerry

Both my wife and myself had bio-energy therapy in October 1987. I had arthritis of the shoulders and I had four sessions at that time. I wasn't able to lift my arm fully and even to take any weight was painful. I'd have to get up twice a night and wave my arms around because I couldn't sleep with the pain in the shoulders. Following the treatment I haven't had a pain in my shoulder. My wife went on five occasions and she had arthritis of the neck. But she feels great since.

When I was getting the therapy on the second day, I could feel it working. I was sceptical originally. I could feel some warming, heat in the shoulders. There was a little pinching or stinging. But even after the fourth time, I still wasn't rid of that pain. It took about a week or a fortnight before I was completely clear of it. The whole thing, while it was easing off, took three weeks.

Martina Flynn, Enniscrone, Co. Sligo

My problem was that I had no power in my fingers. I had a funny sensation in them. I couldn't do anything with them for ages. I was supposed to have arthritis for the last three years. I'm one of those people that don't give in to things; I just keep going. I run a guest house and I have to keep going. I hate going to doctors. I hate taking tablets or anything like that.

Just today I was coming up to the clinic in the car and I was looking at my hand – the muscle had been wasting away on the back and I could now see it filling back in. I just don't know what to say – I can do things again and my hand is fine.

When I was working in the guest house, I just suffered on. I've suffered an awful lot with fluid retention in my hand as well. I used to get water pills but they were no good. All of this started when I was having the children.

I did feel something when I was getting the therapy yesterday. They were pulling me around on the floor every day and I was trying to go against them, just to see. But there was no way I could.

I don't have the full power back yet in my hand, but I can

shake hands or grip things now. I couldn't do that before because it was like an electric shock up my arm when I tried.

James Fahy, Tireallan Heights, Galway

My son Aaron was four and a half months old before we discovered that there was something unusual about him. He was getting sick and he went into hospital. They thought it was pneumonia. It went on and he was getting high temperatures every three weeks. It was every two weeks at first and he might be in hospital for a week. He would come home and they would say he was better. Then he'd be back again. It went on for a long time, four or five months. We were living in the Midlands at that time.

Then we went to Dublin. We got no answers there. They discovered something wrong with his muscle tone and they felt that maybe it was something they could query at a later date. They still didn't give me any answers to the high temperatures. When he would get a high temperature, it would cause him to go off his food and he would go on a drip and he'd lose weight.

He could have got convulsions from the high temperatures. He never got them. He came very close to it at times with temperatures of 105° and 106°, and no explanation from the doctors. They did their best. It wasn't from a lack of trying. We went to every specialist in the country. Finally, one discovered something in the chromosomes. He called it the translocation of genes. It was rare, he'd never came across it before, and as a result the child's muscle tone was affected and we were told that he might never walk. They said that he might walk in his early 'teens but they couldn't tell us for sure. He wasn't on any treatment. They didn't know what to treat.

So we went down to Galway to the bio-energy clinic and on arrival he had a high temperature straight away. He was in for four or five days. The second day, I could feel him boiling hot in my arms when I brought him back to the car.

He started to sit up that week. We brought him to a hospital every week to a physio and even the physio remarked on the improvement in him. And that's only a month ago.

We were here in August and in that month he has progressed now to the stage where he is almost crawling. He will stand if you put him up against something, take the weight off his legs. And the high temperatures have disappeared completely. By the end of that first week, he was sitting up better than he'd ever sat up before. And he's got progressively better since ...

In a month, he has made unbelievable progress. He has improved from the point of view of tone and the high temperatures have disappeared. I'm convinced that it was the bio-energy therapy. It's scientific and it makes sense. I'm not the kind of fellow who believes anything that goes. I've been to faith-healers and what have you. But bio-energy I understood.

The explanation is plausible. Look at the moon and the tides. We know the moon is there and the tides are there and that the tides are affected by the moon. The explanation is scientific and we go along with that because we are intelligent people and we know that it's possible. It's the same with this. These energies can affect you and when you start seeing a result, that helps you understand something. You can't explain it away. I think it's amazing. And the fact is that it doesn't depend on a massive belief in anything. It's a thing that any intelligent person can learn and understand. It's factual and it's there. It's natural and it's nature. It isn't supplemented with any drugs. It's not a money-making racket, it's a genuine thing. They work hard. The fact that they are providing such a service as they are, I think that people should be made aware of it. More luck to them.

But anybody who has a child sick or who is sick themselves, they are the people who know. If it was me personally, I would know if I had been bad and I would know what cured me. If you took a pill and you were cured, you would know what cured you. So, if you have no pain after coming here you know what caused it.

Attracta Horan, Sligo

It was October of last year they discovered I had cancer of my right lung. I had the operation on 31 November. They had to remove all of the right lung with cancer. About a month later, I started to get worse and they did the tests again and came up with the idea that I had liver cancer. So at that stage the surgeon said that there wasn't anything that they could do, only send me home.

I came home and I was very, very ill. I was spending 24 hours a day in bed. Then there was a priest who suggested that I should come to the bio-energy clinic. I hadn't heard about them or I didn't know anything in the world about their work at the time. He said that they had helped him greatly. I came here anyway and from then on I just started to get better and better all the time. I started to go back for my check-ups and they decided to do a second scan in June and that scan proved that the cancer wasn't there any more.

When I was undergoing the therapy, I didn't feel any changes within myself at the beginning. There was nothing at all, whatsoever. I was so weak that the only thing I was hoping was that I wouldn't collapse on the floor when I was out there with them. But the last day of the second session I was here, I did feel a great change myself and, strangely enough, the people outside in the bar remarked to my son when I went out to join him that they had never seen anything to change like me.

And when I went home that day, a young priest came in and said 'What do these people do? What exactly are they doing for you?' And I said, 'If you hold on a minute now, I'll make a cup of coffee and I'll talk to you about it then.' And I didn't realise, I ran out to the kitchen and plugged in the kettle and made the coffee and brought back the two cups. And that's when he said to me: 'Well, I don't know what they've done, but they've certainly given you a great booster some way or other. One minute I come in here, you're in there in the bed and you're like you were dying. Now you're running around your sitting room.'

Now I've had bad times since. I can't say that it was all good because it's not. I've had my rough days and my rough nights since. But I've felt from then on that I was getting better. Every time I have come to them, I have felt better. I wouldn't be here otherwise. I wouldn't come up here for four days. It's tiring. On the third day and you're sitting here a long time – it's an ordeal.

I would definitely say to anybody now that deep down inside me, I do feel God has cured me, but I feel that it is through those people here, that it is through the bio-energy clinic. Because you know, and you can talk to any doctor, there is no treatment you can give for liver cancer. There is nothing you can do. Once you've got it, you've got it and that's it. There's no turning back. They told us that there were two clumps of tissue on the liver and I went back for the scan on the 6 June and they've just gone.

Bill Blake, Kiltimagh, Co. Mayo

I didn't know what was wrong with me. All I knew was that I was caught up in my chest and the doctors couldn't do anything for me. I was taking three or four packets of indigestion tablets a week. I was bad for years. It affected my work and it affected me to the extent that if my dinner was left there on the table, I was afraid to sit down to eat it. As soon as I had my dinner eaten, the burning would start down in my stomach, I had to watch what I was eating. I had to watch what I was drinking. I couldn't enjoy myself at night if I went out for a drink. I can drink anything at all now.

I thought there was a fire in me. There were times you'd get worried about it. You'd go to the doctor and you'd ask the doctor and he'd say. 'Well, you're only taking these tablets and if you're getting any relief, keep on taking them.'

But you only got relief when you had one or two of them in your mouth. An hour afterwards you'd be as bad as ever again.

So I was treated at a bio-energy clinic and after two sessions I was as right as rain. There wasn't a thing wrong with me. That was at the beginning of this year. When I was undergoing the therapy, I didn't really feel anything. It happened just the way I was told it would. I was told that I wouldn't feel any effect for maybe ten days, and in my feet especially I would probably feel pain before I would feel any real relief. And that actually happened. But it wasn't an intense pain. It was a healing process that was happening at the time, but I didn't realise it.

But definitely after the ten days, I could see the difference then. I know the difference now. Before, I'd have pains in my legs if I had to walk a short distance. All the pains in my legs are gone. There isn't hardly a blemish on my legs today. I had to wear a stocking and you could see the veins out through the stocking. You can hardly see them at all now. The whole lot is gone. The heartburn is gone.

I was very, very sceptical when I went to the clinic first. It was arranged for me by others. I didn't go looking for this. They told me at the time that it wasn't faith healing or anything like that, and I didn't know what it was. When I saw what was going on, I was inclined to laugh at first. It didn't strike me as something that was going to be very effective. That was natural enough if you didn't understand it – that you were going to be a bit sceptical about it in the beginning. But I have sent a few patients to them since and I told them what they were in for and I know there was one or two that were very pleased. They got help too.

Patrick Kelly, Omagh, Co. Tyrone

My first clinic was in May 1990 in Bray, Co. Wickow. I had a bad hip and a very sore back. I had the bad hip for years and I had the sore back for about six years. I was totally dependent on a stick. After treatment, I walked out of Bray on the fourth day. I didn't need the stick and I haven't used it since.

I couldn't do anything before that. You could near enough say that I was disabled. On my last day travelling to Bray, I was going into Bus Aras, the bus station, and I had to break my journey to be violently sick. But as I walked across O'Connell Street, something seemed to lift from me. When I was waiting on the bus to Bray, I was a brand new man. That was my hip and my back. I am perfectly sure that bio-energy therapy has helped me. I wouldn't know what it's based on. I wouldn't be able to answer that. But whatever it's based on, there's something there, I am now back to my normal height. After the treatment, I got back the two inches I had lost through being stooped over.

May O'Brien,Threecastle Field, Co. Wicklow

I came for arthritis and Crone's Disease. Crone's disease is a bowel disorder. I was on a lot of medication and I had very bad side-effects from the tablets I was on for both things. I had been taken off the ones for the arthritis: they were causing a lot of kidney problems.

Before last March, I could say that my social life was non-existent. My own life was a misery. I had no comfort going anywhere because I was always looking for a bathroom to change. That's the story when anyone has Crone's. They have no control or at least very little.

I didn't tell the person who was treating me at the clinic I had Crone's disease. I went to get treated for the arthritis. But when I was on the floor, the healer said to me 'What's wrong in your stomach?' I never answered him. I was asked a second time and I didn't answer. But after the second treatment, I had no trouble with Crone's Disease. I was supposed to go into James' Hospital to have the small intestine removed and perhaps part of the large intestine. Now the doctor can't believe that I have no Crone's.

I told my doctor that I had been to the bio-energy clinic. He said 'More power to you.' I was writing to a doctor in Dublin and the treatment I was on involved vitamins and a diet, but that wasn't working for me. At the same time my own doctor said that if I got relief, I should go ahead with it. He's not against the bio-energy at all.

That's another thing. When you go to a doctor about Crone's disease, it's explained to you that there's no known cause and no known cure. The only thing is that if you are bad enough, they will operate and remove part of the bowel. I was told that if they did operate, it did not mean I was going to be cured.

It had got to a joke I think. When you have a complaint that nobody can see, then it becomes a joke. So I had a moon face from the tablets and an extended stomach. That was only one of the side-effects. It just ruins your life. So apart from anything else, I was a kind of drug addict when I came to the clinic. I had come off the drugs and I was in a bad way. I am flying at the moment. It's really unbelievable. I tell people at home and they don't believe it. Now I can go anywhere. I can't thank them or praise them enough.

Brigid Maher, Navan Road, Dublin 7

My problem goes back to 1982. The problem went from my ear to my eye and down my face. What had happened was that one of the nerves had snapped, the main nerve in the face [the trigeninio]. The pain was absolutely excruciating. They brought me into Elm Park Hospital for five weeks for tests. They weren't sure what it was and then they discovered that it was the two jagged ends of the nerve. They decided to take the nerve out as that was the only way of getting rid of the pain. They normally take it out at the ear, but they thought that if they opened up the nervous system to my face and head that they might find something else. They asked me if I would agree to a bigger operation on the basis that they might be able to save my face. So I agreed to having the back of my head opened. They opened it like a letter box, had a peep in, saw what they wanted, cut the nerve that they wanted to cut and closed me up.

I had the belief all along that they would save me, that I wouldn't be left with a numb face. But when I came out of the anaesthetic, my whole left side was numb. When they took out the main nerve, they also took out another little nerve which affects the lubricant in your eye. Every time you blink you secrete a lubricant, but I wasn't doing so. The eye was drying up and I was getting ulcers on it. Now the only good thing was that I couldn't feel the pain of them.

How I knew I had an ulcer was that it would grow over the pupil and I would lose my vision. I'd go to the Eye and Ear Hospital and they would strap up the eye. It would be open for three days, strapped up for a week, open for three days, strapped up for a week – this went on for thirteen months. Eventually I got a second opinion on my eye, because I was getting worried since it was going on for a long time. The second opinion said that if he were my doctor he would stitch my eye up for good. I told this to the first doctor in the Eye and Ear and he said it might be better to do that. So, they stitched the eyelids of my left eye together in January 1984. That's called a torsorophy. I was told that I would never get it reopened because I was not secreting the lubricant.

Over the past six years, I had got the doctor to open it a quarter of an inch. That was a millimetre at a time and he told me in February 1990, when I got a little bit of it snipped, that this was the tolerance level and I was pushing my luck. He asked me not to ask him to open the eye any more because he wouldn't do it. If one of the ulcers burst, I would lose the eye.

I attended a bio-energy clinic in the Spa Hotel in May. I came with my back as a result of a car accident I had had four years earlier and I said nothing at all about my face. I didn't feel a whole lot different on the first or second day.

On the third day, when the healer was working on my face (she had said the previous day that I had trouble with my face, but I told her not to bother about that, that it was my back I was worried about), I said to her that I felt funny under my eye. It felt like a heartbeat. And she said she could feel a movement around my eye, a feeling coming back into my face. I said I didn't believe her. Later it dawned on me that the feeling was all around the eye. On the last day, instead of fighting with the idea that I was never going to get the feeling back in my face, I decided I'd go along with it. When they told us on the last day of the clinic not to believe everything that the doctors told us, I must admit I thought that was a bit dangerous!

I went to the Eye and Ear again after that. This was a prior appointment I had. I met the doctor and said I had been to the bio-energy clinic and he said that he wasn't going to open my eye for me. I said that I hadn't asked him to – this was all said in a very good-humoured, jokey way. I went back a couple of days later and he examined my eye again and then asked me if I would accept full responsibility if he opened my eye. I said I would. He then told me that if the eye needed restitching, I needed to go back to him. He opened it and it's been fine ever since.

Now I use drops and ointment. I think it's a very small price to pay for getting my eye back. It does alter your appearance but I'm more alive, more of a person instead of hiding behind very heavy glasses. If I hadn't gone to the bio-energy clinic, I couldn't have brought up the subject with him. Also, I wouldn't have had the confidence to go through with it. Don't forget that he told me the eye would never be opened since it wasn't secreting lubricant.

When I told him about the feeling coming back in my face, he told me to go back to the neurologist. (I wasn't going to go trotting back to the neurologist who did the operation in the first place, to be quite honest.) This is my fourth bio-energy clinic and the feeling never got beyond the circumference of the eye until today. Today it's going down my face. So, I've my eye sorted out, my hip and three-quarters of my back problem. I'd accepted the fate with my eye as a fact of life. There's a lot to be said for not believing everything the doctors tell you. If I hadn't come to the clinic in the first place, and they hadn't got this feeling around my eye, I wouldn't have been able to have that conversation with the doctor in the Eye and Ear. If I'd never come to bio-energy and never told them about my face, I'd still be going around with a stitched-up eye.

Not many people come with one complaint and get another cured and the original one three-quarters cured. I feel that if you're not cured of a physical disease after coming here, you still get something. The biggest thing you have coming away from a session is hope.

Michael Staunton, Claremorris, Co. Mayo

About six years ago, my daughter was killed in a car accident and that was the start of my problem. When I'd go to bed at night, I'd feel the top of my head pulling down. That went on for about five years or so. I used to be very depressed. I'd go to bed during the day. I wouldn't sleep. Sometimes I'd have to go to the doctor for tranquillisers. I'd sleep then all right, but after a few months it would come back again.

I was very close to my daughter. She was seven years of age. I was all right up to that. I used to be very healthy. I came to the bio-energy clinic and I found them very good. They were the first crowd that put me on the road to relief. About two months ago I went to them. The first evening, I felt something like needles going from the top of my head to the bottom of my toes and I got very bad for a few days then. I got sort of mixed up and contrary the week after. I started to get well immediately and I haven't taken any tablets since I came here.

I find the clinic marvellous. I used to go to the doctor and he would give me tablets for my head, which I would have to take two or three times a day. I'd take them for maybe a week or a fortnight and then I'd leave off them for maybe a month and the same thing would start over again. That was the way I fared out. I find now that the last six years of my life were down. This last two months I've a different outlook on life. I feel that I can get up in the morning and be happy doing a day's work. Up to this, I'd go home and straight to bed. I can sit down now and watch television or whatever I want to do. It has changed my life.

Mary Dolan, Claremorris, Co. Mayo

I am writing to express my most sincere thanks for the wonders you have worked on me. Some 40 years ago, I had the misfortune to fall off an operating table and hurt my back. All through the years, I have suffered constant pain and numbness which, in turn, resulted in headaches, tension in my head and prevented me from sleeping. I had to take sleeping pills a few times a week to ensure some sleep (although I am not in favour of any tablets). I also hurt my left ankle some years ago and suffered agonising pain. It used to swell badly, especially in summer.

When the bio-energy clinic visited Westport in January 1990, I had the privilege of attending and again in February when it returned. After the very first visit I felt different, less pain, less tension and so relaxed; by the end of the week I was a different person and still am, thanks to you – for all the energy you put into me, for all the time you spent on me, for the belief you have in your own powers and the belief you extend to others.

For the first time in over 40 years, I know I have a back which is no longer pain-ridden and part-dead. I have no tension in my head, no pains, my ankle has not pained me since, and last but not least I can go to bed and sleep. I haven't taken a sleeping tablet since January.

I am spreading the news every day of my own cure and

the cures of others I know. My daughter who has been suffering from sinus for years attended a clinic and is now cured. She is so happy. Thanks is so, so inadequate. God bless you and give you all the strength to do what you are doing for many years to come.

Kitty Burke, Claremorris, Co. Mayo

In March of 1985, I was involved in a motor accident. A lorry ran into the back of a stationary car and I suffered a whiplash. I was immediately hospitalised and referred to an orthopaedic surgeon, who prescribed painkillers and exercises (which I was unable to do due to the pain). I wore a surgical collar for eight months. I couldn't do without it for 20 minutes up to September 1987, but gradually got rid of it. The pain was intense and interfered with my sleep. I also had a special orthopaedic pillow. I was diagnosed as having a worn disc and prescribed arthritic drugs.

I found driving very difficult and anything over two miles painful. I often stopped by the side of the road to rest my arms and shoulders, and take painkillers. Doctors told me a whiplash injury never went and I had to learn to live with it. Each day and night I was in pain. All kinds of household duties became a burden: heavy saucepans were agony to carry, hoovering was impossible, as were many other everyday jobs. I suffered severe depression and it took me a long time to accept my status of 'arthritic'. But as the years went by, I grew accustomed to the pain and the drawbacks, and lived accordingly.

Fate led me to the bio-energy clinic where I asked for the healing of another disorder. The therapist told me about the severe pressure in my arms, neck and upper back. I told the him about the whiplash injury and he said he would take the pain away. This was done on the very first day I was treated. For the first time in five and a half years, I slept and woke without pain. It returned briefly after the third treatment, but never since. I've driven long journeys and the pain has never returned. It's great to feel normal again.

Mary McEveney, Claremorris, Co. Mayo

For many years, I suffered from very severe headaches. Nobody knows the pain I went through. I was told that it was different things: migraine, muscular arthritis, my age, my eyes. As the years went by the pain became worse. Hardly a day went by without my having to take painkillers and really strong painkillers at that.

Almost four years ago, I lost my sleep completely and was put on sleeping tablets. The pain in my head got worse and I started to lose my balance. I was unable to concentrate. When I lay down at night on my right side, my head would start to spin. It was like the propellor of an aeroplane starting off in my head and then it would gradually settle down. Life wasn't worth living and all I wanted to do was to lie down and die. I couldn't tolerate any type of noise and I couldn't go anywhere. If I did go out socially, I really suffered from the noise. I had X rays and CAT scans done and I was told that it could be any one of a number of things. I was also told it might be an hereditary disease and it was something I might have to live with. There was a growth at the back of my brain that had to be investigated further with another scan and the possibility that this was cancer was not ruled out.

Before I had that CAT scan, I decided that I would attend a bio-energy clinic. I was let in and sat down. The day I attended I was very sick and in terrible pain. I thought that I would have to go back home before my turn came. As soon as they started to work on me, it began to aggravate me. I began to get sick and the pain started. I really thought I was going to faint. I had to go out and I wanted to fall down, but there was nowhere to lie.

I was treated and from that day onwards, I began to improve. The sleeping tablets were thrown in the fire and my balance began to return. Best of all though, I could turn on my right side at night without spinning. It was a new lease of life for me. The headaches began to disappear and finally I was able to go out and enjoy life, without returning home in pain. This was something that I hadn't done in years. My family could not get over the recovery I had made back to health.

I had a CAT scan done again after that and nothing showed up. It was bio-energy that really helped me. Only for that, I wouldn't like to think what I'd be like today.

These testimonials are just a small sample of hundreds we have received. We continue to get scores each week as more and more people benefit from the therapy. We should point out that if some people are reluctant to attend a clinic, on the basis that we are not professional or do not adopt a professional attitude, there is a Code of Professional Conduct to which all bio-energy therapists adhere. The code is based on the Code of Professional Conduct for the established medical profession and has been suitably amended for our needs. We reproduce it below.

CODE OF PROFESSIONAL CONDUCT

The word 'patient' in this Code of Professional Conduct is to be understood broadly to mean those individuals or groups of individuals who have contact with a Therapist in his or her professional capacity and does not necessarily denote or imply ill health.

The word 'Therapist' is understood to mean any person working with Bio-energy Ireland in any of their Clinics.

The purpose of this Code of Professional Conduct is to help the Therapist to make professional decisions and to carry out his or her responsibilities and to promote high standards of professional conduct.

The Code of Professional Conduct provides only general guidelines, but specific issues will be considered as and when they arise.

Bio-energy Therapy demands a high standard of professional behaviour from Therapists and each Therapist is responsible for his or her practice of the Therapy.

The aim of Bio-energy Therapy is to give the highest standard of care possible to patients and any circumstance or set of circumstances which could place either the patients or the Clinics in jeopardy should be immediately made known to the person in charge of the clinic.

Information regarding a patient's history, treatment and state of health is privileged and confidential, and under no circumstances should this confidentiality be breached, except with the express consent of the patient. From time to time, facts relating to treatment will be recorded, as part of the ongoing care and treatment of the patient. Professional judgement and care should be exercised in sharing such information with professional colleagues. The confidentiality of a patient's records must be safeguarded at all times.

The Therapist has to uphold the trust of those who allow him or her to treat them.

Patients must have appropriate information about making an informed judgement. Every effort should be made to ensure that a patient understands the nature and purpose of their care and treatment. If there is a serious doubt about whether certain information should be given to a patient or not, special care should be taken in such cases.

Any form of sexual advance to a patient with whom there exists a professional relationship will be regarded as professional misconduct. A Therapist must be ready to acknowledge any limitations of competence and refuse, where there is such a limitation of competence, to accept delegated functions without first having received instructions to those functions and having been assessed as competent.

A Therapist shall make known at the earliest possible opportunity to the clinic supervisor any conscientious objection which may be relevant to professional practice.

The Therapist shares the responsibility for the care and treatment of patients with colleagues and must have regard to the pressures and workload on colleagues and take appropriate action if these pressures and workloads are seen to be such as to constitute abuse of the individual Therapist and/or jeopardise safe standards of practice.

Each Therapist has a responsibility to junior colleagues. He or she is obliged to transmit acquired professional knowledge, skills and attitudes by word and example. The Therapist must not delegate to junior colleagues tasks and responsibilities beyond their skill and experience.

The Therapist is responsible for the care and treatment provided by their junior colleagues. The Therapist's responsibility in transmitting knowledge, skills and attitudes and in keeping up the standards of care extends to junior colleagues when they are learning.

The Bio-energy Therapist shall work in close cooperation with members of other health professions in promoting all efforts to meet the health needs of people.

The Therapist must maintain at all times the principle that every effort should be made to preserve human life and where death is imminent, to help to ensure that the patient dies with dignity.

When making public statements, the Therapist shall make it clear whether he or she is acting in a personal capacity or otherwise.

The Therapist will avoid the use of his or her position in the promotion of commercial products in order not to compromise the independence of his or her professional judgement.

The Therapist should not accept any gifts or favours from patients or their relatives which could be interpreted as seeking to exert undue influence or to obtain preferential treatment.

The Therapist will at all times take reasonable precautions to ensure that, from the point of view of his or her health, he or she is competent to carry out his or her duties. It should be pointed out that abuse of alcohol or drugs will adversely affect that competence.

In taking part in research, the principles of confidentiality and the provision of adequate information to enable an informed judgement to be made by the patient must be safeguarded. The Therapist has an obligation to ensure that the research is being carried out by an appropriate body and that the rights of the patient are protected at all times.

DAVOR BULJAN, odvjetnik
YU 57000 Zadar, S. Matavulja 1/3. Telefon: 057 430221, 438555, Telefax: 057 311444

C E R T I F I C A T E

BOARD OF DIRECTORS OF " DRUŠTVA ZA PROUČAVANJE GRANIČNIH PODRUČJA I MENTALNE HIGIJENE " from ZADAR, S. Matavulja 1., C O N F I R M S THAT GENTLEMEN MICHAEL O'DOHERTY AND TOMMY GRIFFIN ARE HONOURABLE MEMBERS AND ARE FULLY AUTHORIZED TO REPRESENT AND ACT THROUGH THE COMPANY " BIO-THERAPY IRELAND ".

GENTLEMEN M I C H A E L O'D O H E R T Y A N D T O M M Y G R I F F I N ARE, BY DECISION OF THIS BOARD, SOLE REPRESENTATIVES WITH ALL EXCLUSIVE RIGHTS.

Z A D A R, 4. 04. 1991.

D I R E C T O R:

ZDENKO DOMANČIĆ

v2

DRUŠTVO
ZA PROUČAVANJE GRANIČNIH
PODRUČJA ZNANOSTI
I MENTALNE HIGIJENE
Z A D A R — S. Matavulja 1/3
Tel.: (057) 438-555

ODVJETNIK
DAVOR BULJAN
Z A D A R — S. Matavulja 1/II
Tel.: (057) 438-555

183

CHAPTER 8

Summary

❈

Bio-energy therapy is a way of treating people that encompasses the whole human being and can therefore have an effect at the physical and non-physical levels. In coming to terms with and understanding this therapy, the West finally has a chance to create a totally holistic approach to health. At this point, it's worth taking a look at the ways in which the body is viewed and treated for illness by different practitioners.

Western medicine has been successful in many ways despite the fact that it has dealt with the physical body almost exclusively and has taken little account of what it cannot measure directly. The map of the body outlines where the muscles, organs, cells and nerves are located, and how they work together on a chemical level. The main drawback of Western medicine has been that it treats the symptoms of the disease rather than the causes. Drugs are used extensively to suppress the symptoms and, in so doing, can allow even more serious disorders to develop over a period of time, especially where drug therapy is prolonged. This has the effect of masking other problems, while weakening the body as a whole. The separation of various parts and functions of the body by Western medicine has also meant that the cause of a problem in one part is examined, whereas the root cause may lie elsewhere.

Psychotherapy takes a slightly different view of illness and how it is caused. Here, the body is viewed as being connected to the mind and it is presumed that emotional and mental attitudes can cause problems. This is at least an advance on the purely physical view of the body. But, like with conventional medicine, the energy aspect of the person is totally ignored and the body's natural ability to heal itself. We have already outlined cases where shock and emotional trauma have left problems at an energy level which may later manifest themselves as physical problems.

Acupuncture takes account of energy flows within the body. This branch of medicine finally brought to the West the systems used in the East for centuries. The meridians or energy lines are manipulated by the use of needles and herbs in acupuncture. The body can be anaesthetised in this way and even the most serious of operations can be carried out while the patient is fully conscious. One of the problems with Westernised acupuncture is that many of its practitioners have been trained in the West and may not have the same degree of effectiveness as their Eastern counterparts.

Homeopathy works on the basis that like cures like, for example a particular poison can be counteracted by the same poison. Unlike Western-style vaccinations, however, the homeopathic remedy does not actually contain any of the original poison. When the remedy is made, the powder of the poison is continually energised and diluted, so that no harmful ingredient is left in the final solution; the aura of energy as the poison is extracted is imprinted into the remedy. Thus the idea is that the energy of the poison will work on the energy system of the person taking the cure. These remedies have proved successful for many people.

HOLISTIC HEALTHCARE

The sort of healthcare we would like to see is one in which all the various disciplines work together towards the common aim of helping sick people to get well. It does not really matter which branch of medicine eventually 'takes the credit' for curing the person. The most important thing is that the sick person is helped as far as is humanly possible.

In practical terms, this approach would mean that we would treat a patient with bio-energy therapy and bring them as far along the road to recovery as we could, but at a certain point, the therapy might not be able to do any more for them. In the case of a car-accident victim, for example, bio-energy therapy can speed up the healing process. But after that has been successfully done, another discipline may be needed, such as physiotherapy, to help the patient along further. The reverse can also hold true. Even at the time of writing, there are various members of the established medical profession who regularly refer patients to us whom they believe can benefit from bio-energy therapy. Thus, a situation where all the disciplines operated a system of mutual referral is the one in which the patient would get the best possible treatment. But, sadly, this day will be delayed until such time as conventional medicine stops being so defensive about its position and agrees that there is more to the make-up of the human being than what they have been taught.

We treat people on an energy level because we believe in a different theory of disease than Western medicine. In our experience, disease in the physical body is the manifestation of an imbalance in the energy field and that imbalance comes about when the free flow of energy is blocked. The causes of that imbalance can be due to any number of factors – physical, emotional, mental. In the case of physical trauma, such as an accident, the healing process can be greatly assisted by first balancing the energy field. Blockages in the energy field need not necessarily be in the same spot as the physical symptoms; in fact, they rarely are. When doctors prescribe drugs to treat this physical location, the real problems, often in another area and at another level, are overlooked. Only a person's inherent ability can heal and the only way to reactive this ability is to treat the energy field.

When we treat people, we are not the source of the energy. Neither do we cause the results. We are a conduit for the energy which allows the person we are working with to help themselves. We look beyond the obvious symptoms, the mere physical, to what is beneath. We explain to our patients what is going on and we share with them the benefit of what we have learned over the years. There is a unique openness about the therapy and the way in which it is administered. This means that we are connected to the person in a very special way during the treatment and both the therapist and patient are responsible for the outcome. This creates an awareness on the part of the patient which, in turn, will give valuable clues to the therapist as to where the real problem lies and at what level.

This interaction or mixing of energies means that both therapist and patient have benefitted as a result of the contact in the clinic situation. We are constantly learning from our patients. Each day's clinic is different and we develop new techniques all the time as a direct result of what our patients tell us. The patient also learns something new from the clinic – they discover a new way of looking at themselves and at life. They begin to think of themselves as having an energy body as well as a physical body and that the former can affect the latter.

We are always conscious that it would be so easy for us to get caught up in an ego trip. The very fact that we are conscious of this means that we can counteract it by not erecting barriers between ourselves and our patients, by not treating people as objects and by always being aware that we are only the vehicle for the energy, not the source. We do not do the healing: the energy that flows through us carries out that task. All of these realisations help to keep the prime motivation in front of us.

We are acutely aware that we all share the same life energy and that ultimately, no matter what our individual religious beliefs, this is what binds us altogether. All life forms have this life force contained within them. In treating a patient, we are treating a member of the human race, a part of nature, and thus a part of ourselves. All our negative attitudes, fears and prejudices have to be forgotten when we are in a clinic situation. We concentrate on helping, as best we can, each and every individual patient that attends.

The role the heart plays in the whole process of healing cannot be overemphasised. Love is associated with the heart and there is a particular type of energy associated with this organ. Basically, it is an energy that has been changed as a result of passing through the heart energy centre. It has been fashioned and tempered by love and is therefore different from cosmic and earth energy. It is an extremely subtle energy that can penetrate deeply to the centre of disease and balance the energy field in a unique way. It also brings about a deep transformation, particularly beneficial to patients suffering a prolonged illness.

The concept, that the emotions affect the organs of the body, is relatively new to Western medicine, but it is one that has gained acceptance. Doctors now firmly believe, for example, that there are certain 'types' of people more prone to heart attacks and cancer than others. Cancer is associated with unreleased grief and trauma. The stomach is affected by worry and depression, the heart by emotional repression. There is a subtle twist to these relationships. Once an emotion has begun to affect an organ, the organ itself will begin to affect the emotion, making it extremely difficult for sick people to help themselves. (This is not to suggest that organs cannot be affected by things other than the emotions; obviously chemical reactions also cause damage.)

When there is a blockage in the energy field, many patients can be induced to think back on their lives and remember what caused the complaint in the first instance, The various stresses associated with the incident can still be locked in the mind and affect the energy field. The memory, too, may take a long time to eradicate. Patients sometimes break down and cry in the clinics when they are being treated: they are in a heightened state of awareness about themselves and every living thing around them. When their pent-up emotions are released, the energy field can then begin to regain its normal balance. It is perfectly natural.

Many factors can cause a blockage of energy. Stress, emotional problems and the way we live today all affect our health, as well as our attitudes. We have drifted so far from nature and nature's secret of the life energy that we have forgotten how to call upon it when we most need it. Many of us spend a lot of our lives worrying and this is one of the most common causes of energy blockage. In the same way that we learned to worry, we can learn not to worry, as we can learn not to be angry or to have negative emotions. In short, we can easily learn to change our way of thinking so that our attitudes and emotions are affected in a positive way.

The techniques and knowledge of bio-energy remained in the East for centuries, hidden from public view. We have no doubt that there is still much to know: in the course of developing the therapy ourselves, we have discovered many techniques that we have never seen written down anywhere. At least part of the reason for this book was to bring this knowledge to the attention of as many people as possible and we hope we have succeeded in that.

The West has much to offer Eastern sciences such as bio-energy. We should be able to develop the technology to monitor and attempt to quantify the transfer of energy that is involved in the therapy. Kirlian photography was instrumental in shaking the assertion of those who said that there was no such thing as an energy field surrounding the human body. Extra-sensitive electronic equipment has also shaken the beliefs of those who asserted that there was no such thing as energy transfer. We are standing on the threshold of a new era for medicine. Being able to detect cancer and brain tumours in the energy field *prior* to their appearance in the physical body has huge implications for the way people are treated and their chances of making a successful recovery from these diseases. It is imperative that scientists devote time and resources to this area of investigation.

With the sort of equipment currently available, we feel that the fate of many researchers in previous decades would be different today. As Harry Oldfield and Roger Coghill point out in their book, *The Dark Side of the Brain*, those people who tried to discover more about the life energy and to formulate new theories about our world met some pretty nasty ends: Wilhelm Reich died in prison, Abrams was hounded by the establishment and died in shame, while a host of other researchers committed suicide or were struck off the medical register. Researchers today are operating in a more open climate, with a responsiveness to new ideas. Part of the reason for this change in attitude is the drug culture.

When drugs first made their appearance on the medical scene, they were hailed as wonder cures for all sorts of diseases and conditions. And for a time it seemed this was the case. Each year saw new drugs come on the market to cure ever more persistent diseases. There was little scrutiny of the drugs that preceded them. As people came to believe more and more in the ability of these drugs to sort out their problems, the doctor began to assume a new role: he effectively took charge of patients' health and they, in turn, handed over responsibility for this aspect of their lives. The symptoms of disease were treated, rarely the cause. The end results of this drug-based culture is that we have thousands of drugs on the market, most of which are not needed and which only serve to bolster the profits of multinational drug companies.

When we first started our bio-energy clinics, we were not aware of the extent and nature of the side effects-of drugs. But over a period of years, we have come to recognise the symptoms that are associated with particular medications and the resultant imbalance in the energy field. We want to stress again that we are not against drugs or doctors, but we are against the blatant abuse of drugs to the detriment of people's health. Increasingly, there are signs that people are not just going to 'keep on taking the tablets'; people are beginning to ask questions about potential side-effects.

From where we stand, this is most encouraging. In our clinics, we are often asked about the possible side-effects of particular drugs and we refer to the standard medical publications for the answers. It seems to us that the greatest challenge facing the medical profession today is to keep their patients' confidence for as long as they continue to prescribe drugs as a means of curing everything.

If energy imbalance causes diseases in the physical body, as we believe, it may be that other researchers are correct when they talk about viruses, bacteria and other organisms manifesting themselves in the physical body at the time of illness. Western medicine holds that these viruses or bacteria are the actual cause of the disease, while Eastern medicine holds that these organisms appear later and actually feed off the disease. The fact that such diseases as cancer have shown up in the energy field long before there was any manifestation at a physical level would seem to support this view. It is a complex argument and one we are likely to hear a lot more about in the coming years. In time, a clear scientific explanation will emerge about how the life energies are manipulated to balance the energy field. We are not scientists and have no deep understanding of the technology involved. Our primary concern is to help people with the ability we know we have developed. It is the job of others to go about explaining it in scientific terms.

Even when people do not benefit directly from bio-energy therapy, we find that in most cases there is a change of attitude for the better. Some, naturally enough, are unchanged on any level or at least so it seems to us. But who knows what is going on in their minds? Those that do change experience 'hope' – the most common reaction: the therapy gives them hope where there was none beforehand and this is the first ingredient for the healing process. The vast majority of patients who attend our clinics have been everywhere, tried everything and found nothing that works. We are their last resort. But no matter what happens within the clinic for these people, we will always attempt to instill hope in them, because without that they have nothing.

Again and again, our patients have told us this, even those who received no apparent lessening of their condition as a result of the therapy. If a patient cannot be helped today, then perhaps something can be done tomorrow. Hope is the single most important gift that we can give anyone. The old adage sums it up – where there is life, there is hope.